Baseballs Don't Bounce
Random thoughts from an injured brain

Forrest Willett

Baseballs Don't Bounce
by Forrest Willett.

THERESA THANK YOU

Forrest

Library and Archives Canada Cataloguing in Publication
Baseballs Don't Bounce / by Forrest Willett.

ISBN 978-0-9880810-1-7

Graphic Design by DrGrafix.ca
Printed and bound in Canada by JB Printing Limited

The Author and Publisher assumes no responsibility for errors , omissions or contrary interpretation of the subject matter in this book.

The events and recommendations in this book are not to be taken as professional medical or recognized therapeudic direction. All readers are advised to seek the services of competent professionals that have experience in the treatment and rehabilitation of those with a brain injury.

This book is dedicated to my wife Julie
who did not give up on me
and believed in me even when
I did not believe in myself,
and to my son and best friend
Hunter who taught me that
baseballs don't bounce.
I thank you both for accepting
me for who I am.

Foreword

Forrest Willett is one of the most remarkable persons I have ever met. It has been my privilege to journey alongside many men and women who have followed the tortuous route from near-death and traumatic brain injury, through many grievous losses, and who have overcome doubt and despair to arrive at the destination where there is a hope for a satisfying, rewarding life. I travelled with Forrest for a good part of his personal journey. It is our good fortune that Forrest discovered that his road back from tragedy involved helping others to find their own way forward. In this book, Forrest extends a helping hand to you.

In this remarkable book, Forrest shares his journey with you. What Forrest has to say can benefit anyone struggling with unwanted, life-changing difficulties. If you or a loved one is struggling with the many challenging consequences of brain injury be assured that in this book you will find knowledge, guidance, encouragement, comfort, and hope. You will also find a hard-earned wisdom. Wisdom gained through the many trials Forrest has faced and the hard lessons he has learned.

Forrest, I thank you for writing this book and I am grateful for your generosity of spirit in striving to help others find their way.

Ever onwards.
Dr. Thomas Davidson

Preface

I was attending support groups for people with acquired brain injury, as well as volunteering in my own community one-on-one with people who have an acquired brain injury, helping them face the fears of the unknown and sharing my story with them. I found it very therapeutic for myself and for the people I am helping.

One day at a support group meeting a woman who is a local author suggested I write a book about the struggles and triumphs I have gone through so that I can share these ideas with the people I cannot reach in person. I took the challenge and here we are.

The process of writing this book has been very challenging given the fact that I had to really relive all of the emotions I had lived before. The good thing is I now know how to handle those feelings and what they mean to me.

My son came home from school one day with the story of Humpty Dumpty. We all remember that story as children, it kind of reminds me of myself and others I have met. Many of us have had a great fall (brain injury) and all the king's horses and all the king's men (Doctors and Therapists) couldn't put Humpty (You) back together again. It all starts with you, you have to want to be put back together again and when you make that decision of course you will need the help of doctors and therapists, family and friends. Just know they cannot put you back together on their own, you must work at it and participate fully in your recovery.

Now that I have picked up the pieces and put myself back together again with the help of many people it is now my mission to help put back together as many people as I can. That is what this book is all about. I have met so many people over the years who felt the same way I did early on in my recovery; basically I felt hopeless "why try?, this is useless" I would think to myself.

Dr. Davidson once told me of people with brain injuries who are now studying to become doctors. I thought 'no way' this can't be, it just seems too unbelievable. Now that the clouds have cleared the way, I can see clearly now that what he told me was true. You can be, do and have whatever you want in life if you work at it.

I would like to share the same message with others and I feel that I have to pass on the things I have learned to overcome this life-changing event and inspire others to become better people.

Please remember to pace yourself. If you try everything at once you will set yourself up for disappointment.

Forrest

"You don't have to be a fantastic hero to do certain things; to complete. You can just be an ordinary person, sufficiently motivated to reach challenging goals. This intense effort, the giving of everything you've got, is a very pleasant bonus." —Sir Edmund Hillary, Mountaineer

"We search for mysteries at the far reaches of outer space, yet there are a great many strange and unknown things going on within the finite space of our own brains.
—Rich Maloof, Writer, Editor, and Musician

Note from the Author

I have asked several people that have crossed my path on my journey to recovery to write their own thoughts of how they saw me through their eyes and the progress I have made. I asked my wife, family, and the professionals that have provided so much help over the years, so that I can share with the readers what really can happen if you are determined to be well and give them hope with their own struggles they may be facing. There are many good books written about an acquired brain injury by doctors and professionals. I found many of them very overwhelming with language only a doctor can figure out or they were thicker than a phone book which was overwhelming to look at.

I wanted to write a book in plain easy language that reads like butter and cuts like a knife, from someone who has gone through it and has come out the other side. I also will touch on subjects that may be embarrassing for some people to talk about. Let me share with you that the only way around these embarrassing or uncomfortable situations is to talk about them and once you can do that it will no longer be uncomfortable or embarrassing. This near death experience has given me a new perspective on life; when you are given a second chance you don't want to waste it. I am grateful to walk and speak and I no longer take things for granted, I treat everyone that I come into contact with the way I want to be treated, with kindness and friendliness and now also treat myself the same way.

Ask yourself this question. If you treated your friends the way you treat yourself would you have any? My hope is that this book may help you or your loved ones through your journey. This book is in no way intended to replace advice of any medical professional. Please contact your doctor before you try anything in this book.

Forrest

"What is important is not what happens to us, but how we respond to what happens to us."
—Jean Paul Sartre, Writer and Philosopher

Testimonials

Julie Willett
My wife

October 6th, 2002, this was the day that our lives changed.

It was a beautiful fall day. We were in the middle of renovating our home. My husband was busy working on our garage. We had a few workers and friends over working on our house. I remember taking my friend and my son who was 2 years old at the time to Barrie for the day shopping. Once we returned, I decided that I would go into the house and make dinner for everyone that was there helping out. During this time, my husband and one of the workers had left in our car. I didn't know where they went and this was not unusual for my husband to go out without telling me; I assumed that they had gone into town to pick up some needed material.

At approximately 6pm, one of my friends had come into the house and said that they had heard quite a few sirens going down the road. At this time I didn't give any mind to the sirens.

Not too long after this, one of our friends who was on the volunteer fire department had said there was an accident up the road and they would have to leave as they were on the fire department. It was one of those moments, when you have that sick feeling. I thought, wow, my husband had been gone for quite a while and he should have been home by now. I didn't know why, I just knew I had to go. I asked my neighbour to watch our son and I said I would be right back.

Once I arrived at the scene, the road was completely closed off. I went as far as I could. Like I said before we had friends that were on the fire department. As Forrest was on this fire department as a volunteer for many years, I went over to one of our friends and asked him about the accident. He just stared at me with tears in his eyes and didn't say a word. It was at that moment that I knew it was my husband that was in the accident. I was told that I couldn't go any closer. My whole body started to shake. A few minutes later a Police Officer came over to me and told me that there was a terrible accident, he wouldn't tell me any details, just that they were going to transport my husband to the hospital. I would have to go there.

When I arrived at the hospital, I was told the car my husband was in had left the road and went airborne into a field, flipping end for end. There was a passersby that had seen the whole thing happen, they believe if it wasn't for that person, they wouldn't have located the car, as the road was not a busy one and the field they landed in was not visible from the road. My husband had been the passenger in the car. I still couldn't understand how the whole scenario had happened or why, I just knew that my husband was now in the hospital with multiple injuries and head trauma.

When I first arrived at the hospital, I couldn't believe it was my husband that I was looking at; I didn't recognize him, his face was swollen and full of blood, he was missing teeth, they had tubes and wires all over him; The thought of him this way still haunts me.

What followed would be many years of rehabilitation. Our lives turned upside down in a matter of minutes. The beginning was the hard part. We were bombarded with people. Lawyers, rehabilitation workers, social workers, everyone came at us at once. My husband had to learn to walk without falling, talk and do everyday chores again like showering, getting dressed and brushing his hair. We also had a successful business that we couldn't just let go. I now had to run our business without his help.

I had to raise our son and help my husband get through his day. It was extremely stressful. Could I have just said "this isn't for me" and walked away? Sure, I suppose I could have. But I didn't, I loved my husband and my family too much. This was something we were going to do together.

And we did.

It is hard to believe it has been almost ten years since the accident. Because of the accident, we have realized that Forrest was given a second chance. Forrest now dedicates his time to helping other people who have sustained a brain injury. He is actively involved with the March of Dimes and also does speaking on brain injury and is now taking university courses and working on becoming a Rehabilitation Support Worker.

I am so proud of my husband and all his accomplishments. He is the most amazing person I know. I love him with all my heart.

Follow your dreams Forrest, you are truly unstoppable.

"The greatest weapon against stress is our
ability to choose one thought over another."
—William James, Psychologist, Professor and
Author

David Fawcett
Investigating officer at the accident

My name is David Fawcett and I recently retired after 37 years as an Operational Police Officer. For the last 15 years of my career, I was an Ontario Provincial Police Constable, assigned to general uniform duties at the Southern Georgian Bay Detachment. This encompasses the areas covered by Penetanguishene, Tiny, Tay and parts of Georgian Bay Townships.

A good mutual friend of ours first introduced me to Forrest Willett back in approximately 2000: Bob Hicks. I was impressed by Forrest's integrity and business savvy. I perceived him to be a friendly, sincere individual. A family man whose heart was in the right place. In my job you learn to read people.

On October 6, 2002, I was on duty in a marked police car. I received the radio call concerning a single vehicle crash in a field off Reeves Road in the Township of Tay. There was witness' information that persons were trapped inside the wreck. I rushed to the scene to find fire fighters and paramedics feverishly working to remove 2 men from the crushed car. Both men were unconscious and covered in blood. They appeared to be very seriously injured. I couldn't recognize Forrest and suspected he was present only because the car came back registered to him. I didn't know the other man who had been driving. It took a full 30 minutes to free them and they were quickly transported to hospital by ambulance. I have to state that we are extremely fortunate in this area to have skilled, dedicated paramedics and fire department personnel.

I interviewed several witnesses at the scene. One man who had been travelling north bound towards the involved vehicle stated he first saw it as it passed over some trees and was just beginning to roll sideways. The car was a large BMW sedan and must have been travelling at an extreme speed to become airborne. It's a testament to the strength of the design and construction of the vehicle that although crushed, it remained relatively intact after the impact with the ground. The car impacted the ground and bounced about 25 feet from a grazing cow.

From the scene I attended the hospital. I was not able to interview either of the injured men. Treatment and care was priority and I know never to get between a doctor or nurse and their patient. I spoke to the drivers son at the hospital, he stated that his father had called him from his cell phone stating that he would be late as he was test driving someone's vehicle, as he was speaking to his father the cell phone went dead.

I determined that family members had been notified and there wasn't anything else I could do to assist at that time. I subsequently completed and filed the appropriate reports. I later heard that Forrest and the driver were both slowly recovering from their serious injuries.

I was lucky to view Forrest's video of his amazing recovery. His very serious head injury would seem daunting and impossible to overcome to most people. But Forrest isn't most people. I am awed by his recovery, the hard work he continues to put toward regaining full function. For all outward appearances he is his old self, still friendly and personable, a good man. I am very happy for him and his family. I am happy to call him a friend.

"Be more concerned with your character than your reputation, because your character is what you really are, while your reputation is merely what others think you are."—John Wooden, American Basketball Coach

Christine MacPherson
Speech-Language Pathologist

I remember the first time I met Forrest with incredible clarity. It was a short time after his brain injury, he had just returned home, and he seemed fragile, passive and very scared. He was in a lot of physical and emotional pain and was confused. As a speech-language pathologist (SLP) I had been asked to meet with Forrest to assess his "cognitive-communication" abilities and to develop a plan for therapy. He wasn't sure why a "speech therapist" was there to meet with him. Despite this uncertainty, Forrest trusted what I had to say and stuck with me, and over a number of years, he worked harder than I can ever imagine. From that first introduction we slowly and surely developed a wonderful therapeutic relationship. Today, many years after we stopped working together in our therapist-client relationship, I am proud to say that Forrest is my friend. I am also proud of Forrest for writing this incredibly valuable book. This book not only tells his own story but offers hope and practical strategies to survivors and their families. Forrest has "walked the walk" and he delivers his clear, functional messages with a delicate balance between humour and compassion. He doesn't sugar coat his journey, and makes it crystal clear that rehabilitation can be a long, hard road. His message is: "I never said it was going to be easy, but it is going to be worth it!".

As a therapist who has been working in the field for almost 24 years I know that rehabilitation, by its very nature, can create a situation where an individual is placed in a passive role. This passive role is necessary in the very early stages of recovery where a person's life hangs in the balance and we need to literally hand over a life to the medical experts. As time passes, and rehabilitation begins, too often this passive role is perpetuated by well meaning therapists, doctors, friends and family members. It is so important to hand back "power" to people who have sustained a brain injury by providing choices, being respectful of decisions and truly collaborating in all aspects of every day life, big and little. Through this book, Forrest has truly reclaimed his "power" and is sharing his incredible story with others. He motivates others to reclaim their own power.

Enjoy this wonderful story of resilience, compassion, inspiration and kindness. Enjoy the frankness, warts and all. Enjoy the funny stories - Forrest can make you laugh, when others would cry. It's all a matter of perspective.

Thank you Forrest for teaching me what it means to not only survive but to thrive.

Forrest, thank you for teaching all of us how to live, not just exist, after a brain injury.

Baseballs Don't Bounce

"To live is the rarest thing in the world.   Most people exist, that is all"—Oscar Wilde

Gary Warman
Occupational Therapist

As a therapist there have been many people that I have had the pleasure of working with. Many have stood out for their abilities or the severity of their injuries or illnesses. Others have stood out for their determination to improve or overcome their losses. Forrest is one of the latter.

I remember the first meeting with Forrest, the look in his eyes reminded me of a deer that had been caught in the head lights of a car. He appeared scared and was not sure what to do or how to respond. Due to injuries caused by the car accident he had gone from a busy successful business man to needing somebody with him all of the time to keep him safe from his own actions.

Forrest worked through many frustrations, feeling that nobody understood what he was going through, realizing that he was not safe to be left alone with his son, criticism from friends for embarrassing things that he did due to a loss of inhibitions, further injuries he sustained due to difficulty recognizing dangerous situations, loss of self-worth due to changes in his business and family life as well as inability to do what he felt he needed to do. These all lead to a change in life's focus and reorganizing his life and focusing on things that he could do in spite of his injuries and limitations.

As Forrest worked through his limitations he was able to change priorities and was able to move towards helping others. He has been able to experience the pleasure of volunteering to help others. He has been able to provide support for others with similar injuries and provide encouragement to those who are struggling with their difficulties.

Forrest's will and determination to get better has been an inspiration for me. I have frequently used parts of his story for inspiration of others who are struggling to overcome their limitations.

Claudia Maurice
Occupational Therapist

I have had the privilege of working with Forrest, supporting him from an Occupational Therapy Rehabilitative perspective soon after his involvement in a serious motor vehicle accident that occurred on October 6th, 2002.

Although I was not his initial treating therapist, I came to know Forrest during those difficult months that followed the accident. It has been a privilege to work with Forrest because since day one, he has is an individual who has put forth his best effort to regain some semblance of normalcy in his life, even during those periods when he felt overwhelmed and confused. Forrest's strength and determination to re-define himself as an individual and to gradually gain acceptance of the changes that have been imposed on him, has always impressed me.

In many ways, Forrest resembled a butterfly that is eventually able to break through its cocoon and eventually spread its wings and fly. Forrest initially presented as an individual who was withdrawn and greatly struggled to accept his changes. In many respects, Forrest did not even understand what his limitations were, which resulted in him experiencing many challenges. Over the course of time, however, and a result of his strong conviction, motivation, determination, and sense of humor, as well as his acceptance of the necessary supports to assist him to move forward with his life, he has been able to redefine the "new" Forrest. It has been my privilege to support Forrest through his lengthy, and at times difficult rehabilitative process. He has definitely been able to spread his wings and is now flying, sometimes even soaring forward. There is definitely no stopping him now!

As health care professionals, we can only assume to understand what it is truly like to have to struggle to cope with the traumatic effects of a brain injury and to forge ahead to redefine the new person that emerges following such a traumatic and devastating event. What I have learned over the years, however, is that such individuals have remarkable resiliency and the ability to move forward to lead productive and meaningful lives. Although they may have an altered life path, they are able to evolve into remarkable individuals who demonstrate strength, courage, and at times a wonderful sense of humour. It never ceases to amaze me, in regards to how much I continue to learn from my clients. I have also come to realize that the key to working with individuals who have suffered life-changing events, is essentially to listen to them and "never say never" with respect to their abilities to achieve what is truly meaningful and important to them.

Forrest has taught me that no matter how high that mountain may seem, that maintaining a positive attitude, sense of humour, strong conviction, level of dedication, and willingness to work with those that are there to assist them, can result in assuming a new purpose in life, as well as a sense of productivity, meaning and overall fulfillment. Life has many curves that at times can be painful to negotiate. With the right attitude, however, and a willingness to work hard, these curves can lead to an amazing path of recovery.

Thank you, Forrest, for the opportunity to be part of your journey. I know that you will only continue to spread your wings and fly, and capture the hearts of other as you have done with mine.

"Take chances, make mistakes. That's how you grow. Pain nourishes your courage. You have to fail in order to practice being brave."
—Mary Tyler Moore, Actress

Bob Hicks
Long time friend

My name is Bob Hicks, I have known Forrest for approximately 25 years and happy to call him a friend. Forrest and I first met through our being in the automotive industry; he was relatively young but had already established a very good reputation with his clients and community. He was involved in many community programs one which included him having to sleep in a skyjack suspended high in the air for a charitable organization, with very uncooperative weather that night I might add.

I knew Forrest before he was married and he was always popular and respected. Everything that Forrest attempted seemed to turn out golden. A common quote heard when talking about him was "everything he touches turns to gold". There were some stresses but it never showed.

After leaving the car business he developed a business with franchises across the Simcoe County/Georgian Bay area, and business was thriving and growing by leaps and bounds. He was also buying, fixing and selling houses and then came that day....

I heard the stories from law enforcement, friends and firemen, the stories were horrific and the pictures of a young man that I knew very well were unrecognizable. I was sure that "IF" he recovered things would never ever be even half way normal again.

I have to give credit to his wife as she stuck by his side through the very difficult times to follow, and I am sure that most women faced with a seemly hopeless future with her husband would have taken the easy route and left. And most people would not have blamed her, but she persevered. Also to be raising their son and now her "new child" Forrest as he now with his brain injury was almost child like as well. She truly has shown that a supporting wife is a true blessing to his ongoing recovery and a very very hard job.

I know first hand how hard recovery is. My son has an acquired brain injury that we have been dealing with for 3 years and the simple things that frustrate to no end, such as memory loss, fatigue, and low drive. I am glad to have Forrest as a resource and friend to my son Joel as they can speak and talk out frustrations together.

And now if you meet Forrest or my son it would take a lot of scrutiny to find or see a problem, but they are dealing with issues of memory loss and feeling of "what am I forgetting' as well as other issues every second of the day.

I have to say there is only one thing that Forrest continues to work on very hard with no improvement and I see how frustrated he gets and that is his golf game.

Forrest is now back driving, buying and flipping houses, golfing (although not very well) and recovering from a brain injury that people told him would be the end of a productive life.

Please share this book with someone you know in this position, as Forrest is living proof you can come back from a brain injury. He is a great inspiration to all that know the story including my son and our entire family. I know complete recovery will be years if ever, but where you are now from where you came is a Miracle.

I am proud that you call me your friend and it is my privilege to be able to write this for you.

"Goals. There's no telling what you can do when you get inspired by them. There's no telling what you can do when you believe in them. And there's no telling what will happen when you act upon them."—Jim Rohn

Forrest Willett

My name is Forrest Willett. I drive a pick up truck. I like to wear blue jeans, running shoes and old t-shirts, most of them I purchase from the Salvation Army or Goodwill, two charities I fully support and hope you will too. I like golfing with my buddies, the most extreme sport I play.

I am one of seven people left in the world who is not on facebook. I don't use a computer to keep track of my friends. I like to get a phone call from Johnny saying "what's up?" or go knock on Doug's door asking if we're on for golf on Sunday. I don't like to spend my time reading emails from Lane Pearson asking if I remember when his sister put gum in my hair in Grade 6 and I had to shave my head?

Get out and visit some people, call an old friend on the phone, I guarantee that it will make you feel a lot more human!

Forrest

Baseballs Don't Bounce

"Human Kind". Be both
—Forrest Willett

Introduction

It was a warm fall day in October 2002. The kind of day you wear a t-shirt trying to stretch out the warmth before the cold days of winter. The trunk of my car was filled with tall grasses and cornstalks, not for Thanksgiving decorations. My car had flipped end for end several times and landed in a farmer's field. An eyewitness told police that it looked like something out of the movies, he couldn't believe that what he had seen was real. He checked on us briefly then went on to the farmhouse to call 911.

I have no recollection of the accident or the weeks to follow. I don't even remember leaving my driveway. I do remember earlier in the day. I was working on my house and received a phone call from a person in Toronto interested to come and test drive my car. I had for sale a BMW 540.

A guy that I had hired to do the drywall on my addition had brought his brother along with him that day to help him finish the job as he was running behind. It was the first day I had met him. He was admiring the car in the driveway and I told him it was for sale and that someone was on their way to test drive it today. He stated that he was looking for a car and asked if he could test drive it. I said sure, he seemed to be a very responsible and pleasant person in his mid forties. It was never in my character to prejudge or ask someone if they could afford something and still is not in my character, as I have known many men in dirty old coveralls who could buy fancy cars with hundred dollar bills.

So off we went. I sat in the passenger seat and.......................... that was it.

I have no memory after that, not even pulling out of the driveway. After the police did their report it was revealed that the driver was talking with his son on the cell phone telling him he would be late for supper and that he was trying out a car; then as his son said, the phone went dead.

The police closed the road for several hours to complete their investigation. They brought in a technical traffic team to investigate the crash scene, and could determine from the skid marks, impacts and distance from where we first crashed to where we finally ended up that the speed we were traveling was between 160 to 180 km/hr.

All it took was one split second and our lives were changed forever. We were both left with traumatic brain injuries; through later testing I was declared catastrophic by the Glasgow outcome scale which states I had a permanent loss of fifty-five percent or more of my mental and behavioural self. This would be my second brain injury, the first occurred when I was two when I fell down the basement stairs and suffered a sub-dural hematoma which required surgical intervention to relieve the pressure from my brain.

After the car accident when I came home from the hospital I did not realize how much I had changed; I felt that it was the people around me who had changed. To try and imagine what it would feel like may seem impossible to some but just for a moment try to think about this. Remember your worst cold or flu when you laid in bed for days with no energy or ambition just wishing it would go away. Now add on to that the worst headache you have ever had. Think about watching a movie in a foreign language with subtitles you can't understand but everyone else can, then throw in a little bit of loneliness, anxiety and anger ... no, throw in a lot of loneliness - the kind you feel when you're surrounded by people but you still feel you are all alone. That is only a glimpse of what many people with acquired brain injury will experience every day.

For years I was confined inside my own negative thoughts and emotions, feeling as if someone or something had my brain locked up in a vault somewhere. It turns out it was locked up in a safe right in my own head and all I had to do was find the right combination to unlock it to free my mind and see what was possible for myself.

Everyone's brain is different and everyone's injury is different, like fingerprints: no two are the same. While searching for the right combination to unlock my brain vault I discovered that although everyone is different, many of the symptoms, problems and obstacles were the same and so were the solutions. I have realized I am not in this alone.

In this book my hope is that you can find some solutions to free yourself from the things that may be holding you back from moving forward.

If you find just one thing helpful that is one more step in the right direction.

This is not a 'how-to' book, rather a 'how- to –think- about- things' book. It is a book full of ideas, thoughts and life lessons I have experienced on my journey through traumatic brain injury.

The purpose of me writing this book is to help the reader understand what goes on in the mind of a brain injured person and to let people know there is hope and help; you are not alone.

If you have a brain injury or know someone with one, my hope is that it can be detected early on. Studies have shown that early intervention is effective against many of its most damaging consequences such as depression, anxiety and ultimately alienation. Not so long ago you would hear things like "Uncle Jim was never the same since he came home from war. He was very angry with no patience or any drive to do things like he used to do. That's why Aunt Claire left him". Well, maybe Uncle Jim had a brain injury and it went undiagnosed.

It has been nine years from the time of my accident to the writing of this book; five years ago I could not read a book, now I am writing one. WOW, things can change! Nowadays you hear of head injury on a daily basis in the news. "A woman was sent to hospital with a head injury", "two soldiers received head injuries in a roadside blast", "Sydney Crosby out of hockey again due to head injury." It's everywhere and always has been. You just hear more about it now than years ago, as doctors learn more about the brain and how it works. I believe the more people who understand what a brain injury is about will make a better world for everyone.

No one would ever say "It's just cancer, get over it". Brain injury is real, just as depression is real. It is an invisible disability.

Brain injury affects different people in different ways and I don't want to trivialize or exaggerate other people's experiences.

I can share with you what has happened to me and the struggles I have overcome and lessons from myself and others who have shared there stories with me.

The great turnaround in my life came to me that day I discovered baseballs don't bounce. As you will read later in the book it was about two and a half years after my accident. I hope these ideas will help you discover your great turnaround long before that. If I can you can too. I'm nobody special, I don't have a university degree, I struggled through school, as a matter of fact with the help and encouragement of my therapists I went back to school and graduated from grade 12 at the age of 37. It was both very humbling and a great feeling at the same time. I was also awarded the Lieutenant Governors award for community volunteering.

I hope this book will help you take months or even years off your recovery time. Let our failures be your lessons and let our victories be your inspiration.

"Become addicted to constant and never- ending self-improvement."
—Anthony J. D'Angelo, Author

My car ... or I mean what's left of it.

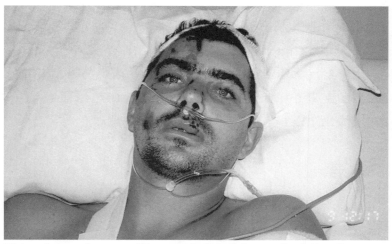

This picture is me, although I didn't know it at the time.

At the Hospital

About ten days after the accident my future was looking pretty unclear. Come to think about it everything was looking pretty unclear back then. My whole world seemed to slow down as if we were all moving under water.

"Desire is the key to motivation, but it's the determination and commitment to an unrelenting pursuit of your goal – a commitment to excellence – that will enable you to attain the success you seek."
—Mario Andretti, Race Car Driver

This section pertains particularly to the caregiver.

This can be a very confusing time for everyone, so it is important to remain calm at the hospital. Whether your loved one has had a stroke or has been in a car accident you must realize that they are going through a very stressful time themselves. Adding your stress and fears on top of that will only compound the problem. Just know that they are in the best place they can be with the best care available to them at this time.

In the unexpected event of an accident, word spreads like wildfire. So you may find yourself in the hospital with many other concerned people, friends, co-workers, relatives, neighbours and other family members. And every one of them may be experiencing many different emotions and these emotions will come and go at different times.

I can't imagine what the family members must be going through, so I asked my wife, friends and some family members what some of their emotions were at the time of the accident. Some have said time stood still, and things they took for granted before have now changed forever. Their priorities have changed. Here are some more feelings they experienced.

Shock and denial-you may have a hard time believing what just happened is real, you're in shock or you can't believe that this just really happened. Everything is a blur and you may have a hard time remembering information or conversations that are going on.

Fear and panic-these are common reactions after such a traumatic event. Your fear is intense because of the unknown. Will he live? Will he die? The panic continues until the patient is stabilized. Some of the feelings you may experience will be a racing heart and inability to sleep, decreased appetite and a lot of crying. Shock, numbness, disbelief, panic, helplessness and hopelessness are a few more common feelings. Your emotions may feel like you're on a roller coaster.

Anger-many people feel angry; "Why did this happen?" They may be angry at themselves for different reasons, they may be angry at the doctor for not getting the answers that they want to hear. Try to have some compassion in this area. The doctors and nurses are trying their best to help your loved one survive and are under a lot of stress themselves. So it is important to control your anger and aggression in the hospital. You may even be asked to leave at some point if you cannot control your emotions.

Guilt-this is another reaction that many people feel. Some people feel they may have been able to prevent the accident, even though in most cases they could not. Some people say, "Why could it not have been me instead of them?" especially if there is a child involved. You may also experience visitors who you have not seen in years, but who for some reason also feel guilty, whether it's for not keeping in touch or something that happened in the past that was not cleared up. Whatever their reason is, it may be their guilt that has brought them there. I have seen for myself a father coming to the bedside of his son in the hospital. His mother told me the father had not been around for fifteen years and I would imagine it was guilt that brought him there.

Anxiety-your anxiety may be floating along like a feather in the wind, up one minute with the hope of recovery and down the next with complications and setbacks. This is where it is very important to express your feelings and concerns with your family, friends and doctors. These feeling may go on for weeks and change day to day, hour to hour. It may seem as if you are in a dream from which you hope you will soon wake up.

"One today is worth two tomorrows; never leave that till tomorrow which you can do today."—Benjamin Franklin

Reduce stress at the hospital

What can be done at the hospital to reduce the fears and anxieties of yourself and those around you, and also make your stay a little less stressful?

For the caregiver;

Remain calm, panic and anxiety will only worsen the situation, when friends or family members see you panic they too will panic. Then the anxiety is in control, not you.

Ask the crowds to go home and let them know that you will notify them if any news comes to you.

Put someone in charge of all notifications, someone who is not at the hospital and who will be able to phone people, or someone that the concerned people can phone for information instead of calling the hospital steadily or looming around the waiting room. This person could also be in charge of visiting, as it is important not to overwhelm the patient; he/she needs rest in order to heal properly. Too many visitors in one day can cause fatigue and stress which will slow the healing process.

Give the main caregiver a break. You cannot expect a husband, wife, mother or father to sit at the bedside of an injured person for days and weeks on end without it affecting their own health, be it mental or physical; they must take a break or they could end up in the hospital themselves. So have some chosen caregivers that would sit by your side while they take a break, even if it is just going for a walk outside of the hospital and getting some fresh air. I would suggest going out for dinner with a friend or relative or have a good night's sleep in your own bed to get your mind off things for a while, which would give you a well deserved mental break.

When people do come to visit meet them out

in the hallway for a quick briefing. Make them aware of what they are about to see. This will reduce some anxiety or shock especially if the person is disfigured as I was. My teeth were missing and my face looked like a swollen basketball covered in blood and bruises with many tubes and wires all over my body. Although I have no memory of being in the hospital whatsoever, I have heard stories of others who do remember, and of people coming to visit them. One that sticks out was a grand-mother coming to see the grandson without being briefed. She broke out hysterically crying "Oh my poor baby look at your face, I can't believe it, it doesn't even look like you!" That kind of visit compounds the stress and fears of not only the patient but the grandmother and whoever else was in the room. Yet if she had been briefed as to what she might see she may have been able to stay calm and that would also keep the patient calm.

The other thing to keep in mind is if you're going to talk about the patient in a negative way go out in the hall and shut the door. Just because a person is unconscious doesn't mean they don't know you're there and can't hear what you are saying. So keep your talks positive. Never talk negative about the person in front of them (or at all). What I mean by this is don't announce to the visitor, "things don't look too good for Billy' or "the doctor thinks he may not be able to speak again". These are just negative thoughts, get them out of your head and think positive, because good things will come. I have met many people who were told they would not talk or walk again and they are now talking and walking fine.

When speaking to the patient, assume he or she understands what you are saying. Speak in a comforting, positive and familiar way. Speak clearly and slowly about familiar people and memories. And when I say speak slowly, I don't mean in slow motion. I just mean slow enough for the person to understand; the patient is not deaf and is not stupid! Remember, the person has not lost their intelligence; it just may take a little longer than usual to comprehend what is being said.

If a person is in a coma perhaps you could play their favourite television show or their favourite music. A friend of mine, Sam, who was in a coma for months, said, "Do not ever underestimate the power of positive talk when you are in a coma." He went on to tell me that his wife was beside him every day, always talking positively to him, reading to him, playing music and watching the television just as if he was there watching it with her. And it was worth all of her time she spent with him. They now have a great life together and a beautiful daughter.

Get a notebook or day-timer and write down important information. You can use this to keep track of questions you want to ask the doctors and other healthcare professionals. So often they are in and out very quickly while dealing with the patient and it slips your mind to ask the question you have been waiting to ask until after they had left the room. It is also helpful to share this information with the patient in the future and allow them to gauge how far they have come. This can be very positive to their self-esteem and outlook on life in a world that does not seem very positive from a patient's view looking outward at this time.

Express your feelings. Talk to your family and friends about how you are feeling. This will relieve a lot of stress off your back in a time when you feel overwhelmed and remember, it is okay to cry. When visitors are present, focus on the patient. Keep the number of visitors to one or two people at a time. Visits should be kept short. Turn off the television and radio while visiting. Too many distractions can overwhelm the patient.

"Never think that you're not good enough yourself. A man should never think that. People will take you very much at your own reckoning."—Anthony Trollope, British Novelist

Coming home

Being discharged from the hospital or rehabilitation centre may be a big relief for some people, but it also may be a little frightening for the patient. It may sound odd but some people feel more comfortable in the hospital than they do coming home, just knowing that in the hospital they are safe and secure and no one is going to harm them. It may be a security blanket for some people. And for some it is the only familiar place they know at this time.

For me, coming home was a different experience because it was no longer my home that I once felt comfortable in. It was a new world for me. Little things that seemed normal at one time, such as our dog barking, now sent me over the moon. When he would bark I would almost jump out of my skin with fear. The same would happen when someone would slam the door. I guess I had so much anxiety built up it took very little for me to feel overwhelmed.

I also had some new faces in my house that I did not recognize, such as home care workers and support workers. This was all very new to me in an uncomfortable way, having a stranger bathe me while my wife was at work. Even the bathtub was different, now outfitted with a chair in it and handlebars on the wall. I have to say it took some getting used to, this new home of mine.

"The dishwasher is running and I cannot understand what you're saying." I don't know why but such little distractions as a dishwasher running, the television on or the radio turned low would distract me to the point where I would not understand what a person was saying when they were talking to me. Often I would just nod my head with a blank stare on my face as if I understood what they were saying, thinking "Your lips are moving, but I have no idea what you're saying".

So keep this in mind when you come home with your loved one. It is important to keep distractions minimal. We already have a problem with being distracted easily. This can also be confused with memory problems. Yes, I'm admitting it. "Sorry" to all the doctors and therapists who explained this rational to me many times and I doubted it every time. I can now look back and put it all together and I hope this will save you a lot of time and frustration. I would be angry with my wife and say things like, "Why the hell didn't you tell me John called?" And she would reply, "I did tell you when you were watching the television this morning." You see, I was distracted but I would just blame everything on a bad memory at that point. It was an easy out and that was a constant excuse I would use. "I forgot".

So remember, the less distractions you have, the less you will hear "I forgot".

To the patient

Just as you would in the hospital it is important to have a team leader in the beginning to do the things such as keep family, friends and co-workers informed on the progress of the patient, as well as co-ordinate visits and phone calls. Once you come home from the hospital it is easy to become overwhelmed by all the sudden attention from family, friends and relatives. So try to keep visits short and have a break in between as fatigue is one of the major problems I have with brain injury and that I still struggle with. You must understand that just talking to a visitor for 10 minutes would make you just as tired as you would be from running a marathon. It sounds odd but it is true.

I think it is very hard for someone who has not had a brain injury to understand what is going on. You may hear comments such as "Christine looks great now that she is home, but I just can't understand why she wants to sleep all day". After suffering a brain injury you need a lot of rest to heal. But you also must understand the things you took for granted before, like doing your everyday routine, is now a major effort. In trying to do those things, fatigue just compounds your frustration. Someone once said to me there are twenty-seven steps to making a peanut butter sandwich from opening the bread to eating the sandwich. But when you do it everyday it seems as easy as 1-2-3.

And remember you can't do this alone, if you think you can you're only fooling yourself. Just look at anyone who has had a successful recovery and you will see that they did not do it alone, you will see that they had a great support team made up of friends and family and professionals who were all positive and supportive during the good times and bad. It is also worth mentioning that everyone I know who has had a successful recovery of any extent had to release the human emergency brakes that were slowing them down and what I mean by that is getting rid of, or spending considerably less time with those people that drag you down and fertilize the weeds of depression and hopelessness.

To the caregiver;

When your loved one comes home allow him/her time to rest and give time to heal. You may even have to schedule rest time into their day- timer, as I had to do. If it wasn't into my day-timer, I usually wouldn't rest, and then I would be too tired to even think. I would usually rest between one and three o'clock; that is when I found that I would become most tired during the day.

When someone offers help, accept their help. You can't do this alone; you have a long road ahead of you so please take my advice, accept the help being offered but be specific about how this person can help. Allow them to stay with your loved one while you go shopping or prepare meals. If you have other children allow a friend to take your children to a movie or play outside while you can get some well needed rest.

People must realize that it is not just the brain-injured person's life that has been turned upside-down, it is the whole family's. And it is the whole family that will have to readjust to this new life with brain injury. Yes it does suck! And it is not nice, but know that with your support and help it will improve dramatically. The sooner you accept what has happened, the sooner you can begin your journey to recovery.

"Far and away the best prize that life offers
is the chance to work hard at
something worth doing."
—Theodore Roosevelt, 26th American President

Some People with Brain Injury will not see a Hospital.

I have met many people over the years with brain injury, who were not diagnosed at a hospital at the time of their injury for several different reasons. Some people believe if they hit their head that it's just a headache and it will go away and they don't take it seriously until someone points out irregularities in the person's behaviour or cognitive abilities.

Here are a few examples of people I have met with brain injury who did not seek immediate medical attention and their reasons for it. One woman was doing laundry with a stackable washer and dryer; she opened the dryer door, bent down and pulled the laundry from the washing machine. As she stood up quickly she knocked herself out on the dryer door. Luckily she had a friend with her to explain what happened when she came to, so she took a few aspirins and laid down until the headache would go away. She was a school teacher who in the coming months found she could no longer do her job. She is doing well now even though she's not teaching anymore.

Another person I met slipped on some ice on the sidewalk leaving him with a large lump on the back of his head. Not thinking much about it he took aspirin and Tylenol for a few days thinking he could shake it off. As it turned out the only thing he shook off was his relationship with his wife. She noticed the differences in his behaviour and thinking and brought it to his attention which angered him. He was in denial and refused any help for years eventually finding himself living alone. He is making tremendous progress now that he has accepted what has happened and is working on improving his behaviour and cognitive abilities. I wish him all the best in the future, he is a good person who just needs some help.

If you know of someone who has had an injury to the head please talk to them about seeking help or at least getting it checked out. The following are some of the common symptoms you may see in a person who has had brain injury. Remember everyone is different - these are only some common symptoms. The best person to consult and confirm this would be a doctor.

-Changes in, or unequal size of pupils

-Chronic or severe headaches

-Coma

-Fluid draining from the nose, mouth or ears (may be clear or bloody)

-Loss of consciousness, confusion or drowsiness

-Loss or change in sensation, hearing, vision, smell or taste

-Memory loss

-Mood, personality or behavioural changes

-Restlessness, clumsiness or lack of coordination

-Speech and language problems

These are just some of the symptoms a person with brain injury may be experiencing; again I am not a Doctor so if you notice these symptoms in a person please get them to a doctor.

"The secret of success is doing the common things uncommonly well."—John Davidson Rockefeller Sr., American Oil Magnate

Mirror Mirror on the Wall

Will I be the Same at All?

This would be a question that would haunt me for a long, long time; it's a perfectly normal question and one that comes up quite a bit. Even after all my physical injuries seem to fade away when I looked in the mirror I still wondered, when was I going to wake up and be me again?

Have you ever missed yourself so bad?

I have.

Sometimes I would cry myself to sleep wanting nothing more than to have the old me back. I guess the easiest way to describe that feeling to people who may not understand is that of a small child who sobs and cries himself to sleep repeatedly saying "I want my mommy". It is a want so bad, that not only are you crying you are physically shaken and drained of all your energy.

When will I be normal again? What is normal?

These are some other questions I found myself asking again and again; it took a long time to realize there is no right or wrong answer to these questions. Brain injury and depression made me question what society teaches us from an early age about what normal is. Here in North America most of us are brainwashed to think as you grow older to be normal you will have a wife, two and a half kids, a dog and a mortgage. "Just like the 'Leave it to Beaver' television show."

So now when I hear someone ask the question, "will he or she ever be normal again?" I guess I wouldn't have the answer they are looking for unless I truly knew the person. You see everyone's version of normal is different. Can someone with a brain injury and depression learn to live a relatively normal social life? I think that would depend on the extent of the injury and how that person defines a social life. If someone is very shy and does not have a brain injury is he or she more or less normal than a very outgoing person with a brain injury? There is no one-size-fits-all way of behaving for anyone in the world.

The person who cuts my hair is openly gay. Is he normal? Absolutely he is. Does this bother me? Not one bit.

Twenty years ago people may have said that that was not normal, and nowadays it has become very normal and acceptable. As times change so do people's perception of what normal means to them.

I have found it in myself to have fewer rules as to how people live their lives, although it took a near death experience to change the way I thought. I think I am a better person for it. This kind of thinking also reduced a lot of stress on me by not worrying so much about how other people are living their lives.

Before my injury I would often say to people, "get over it", to whatever problem they may have whether it was a sore back or a relationship breakup. "It's not normal to be whining about your problems for so long", I would say.

I can say now that it has been over nine years since I have said "get over it". Back then I had no idea, nor any inclination to want to know anything about brain injury, depression, anxiety or any other type of mental illness. I now know you don't just "get over it". If I met someone who stuttered quite a bit or forgot what they were saying in the middle of a conversation I would think to myself "that's not normal," and here I am today doing the exact same thing and believe me it is now normal to me. I think if everyone stopped comparing themselves and others to what they see on TV or what they think their version of normal is and had fewer rules how other people live their lives the world would be a better place.

"Confidence is; Going after Moby Dick in a rowboat, and taking the tarter sauce with you. A Bull fighter who goes in the ring with mustard on his sword."
—Zig Ziglar, Author and Speaker

Julie,
Close Friend

Meet Julie Edwards, a close friend of over 20 years and one of the people I have regrettably told, to "get over it"! Her husband John is my closest friend and our sons are also best friends.

We have been through many things together. When their son Tyler was born I was able to see him before anyone. After delivery, Tyler was taken to the next town about an hour drive away by ambulance and his mother and father would be transported later.

I owned a business in that next town and happened to be there that day, so I went to the hospital and said "I am here to see baby Edwards". The nurse just assumed I was the father so they let me in and told me that he would be tall like me because he has long feet! I still remember that day.

The reason I often told Julie to get over it was because she had a brain injury. Two years before my accident Julie was a passenger on a snowmobile that had hit a stone wall in white out conditions, she sustained a catastrophic brain injury and in the years to follow she went through many different therapies such as speech therapy and occupational therapy, after all of the physical wounds had healed I was stumped as to why she still needed so much help? Why can't she just get over it? She looks ok.

I can say now looking back I thought that maybe it will just all go away one day and things will be back the way they were before the accident I also wondered was all this in her head? I was not knowledgeable about brain injury even though I had sustained one as a child and maybe there was a part of me that just didn't want to know.

I remember one day making her laugh so hard she cried in pain because she just had reconstructive surgery on her jaw. Two years later the rolls were reversed she was visiting me in the hospital, feeding me Ensure® through a straw after I had reconstructive surgery on my jaw to rebuild my upper jaw bone, only this time I wasn't laughing. Over the next few years she would see the therapists come and go from my house, many of the same therapists I might add, and I have to say that she never once said "get over it" to me and I have not said it myself since.

Julie has also made a remarkable recovery and has been an inspiration to me over the years and is also an inspiration to many other brain injury survivors showing us all you can live an exceptional life despite this invisible disability, I am lucky to have her as a friend.

This story is important to remember, when you have a friend recovering from a brain injury please be there for them because you don't know if it will happen to you and if it does you will wish you have some good friends around to support you. I was one of those people who said that it would never happen to me!

Baseballs Don't Bounce

You miss 100% of the shots you don't take.
—Wayne Gretzky

Where are all my friends?

About a year after my accident I was questioning where all my friends were. It seems they had disappeared and left me. The friends that remained I could count on one hand and they are still there for me today. Thank you Johnny, Denis and Bob for sticking it out with me and not giving up and also for your sense of humour.

What happened? Taking a step back and looking at things with you right now I can honestly say, I drove some of them away myself with my constant negativity and self-pity because all I wanted people to know is how bad things were for me, and let me tell you that gets old real fast.

I also can tell you in the early times of the recovery I didn't have very much genuine interest in other people and their feelings. I focused totally on myself. I also talked a lot about how my brain injury had ruined my life and often argued with people, and after doing that for a while I was totally by myself and alone.

Some friends that moved along were afraid or confused not knowing what to do, say or expect so the easiest thing to do for them was to disappear. That is human nature and has nothing to do with you. Don't take it to heart as I did. Let it go.

Some friends just move on in life whether you have a brain injury or not. They meet different people and find different interests. Don't take this personally.

If you are a friend of the injured person, my plea to you would be stick it out through the good times and the bad. Remember you are friends and there's something about this person that brought you together in the first place. Just try to remember those good qualities they are still inside.

Looking back I can give you some tips of things to avoid and things that helped me with my friendships.

**Things that drove friends away
(avoid these at all costs)**

I interrupted people often to get what I
wanted to say out there

I asked people very personal and
inappropriate questions

I wouldn't listen to or take others' advice
or suggestions

I would not accept friends' offers of help

I did not think before I spoke so I said a lot
of things that I should have kept to myself

**Things that helped mend and create
new friendships**

I worked on accepting myself
just the way I was

I became a good listener; people would
then listen to what I also had to say

I joined a support group that was a
tremendous help

I learned to think before I spoke; this way
I do not say things I will regret

I learned to avoid sharing all my negative
thoughts with others

If I could write a letter to my friends back then this is what it would say...

Dear friends and family,

I am here with you, I really am. Although it may not look like me or sound like me, it is still the same old me inside.

This body is just a vessel to get around in, the engine inside(my heart and soul) is still the same; I am in here and I can understand what you're saying, I just cannot reply at this time in the way you are used to. Please do not abandon me, for your love and hope is all I have.

I am scared to death and don't know what to do, so please bear with me in the months and years to come. I need you now more than I have ever needed you in my life. Your presence alone has more healing power than any medical device and your love and support will guide me through these rough times. Don't give up on me as I have not given up on you. Although I may not smile I want you to know your presence makes my day, and your smile is as soothing as the warm sun on my face. When you smile at me, please be genuine. It breaks my heart to see that awkward forced smile that tells me you are scared and unsure (I can tell by the look in your eyes). Remember you are still the same friend that I always knew.

Talk to me as you have always talked to me but just be clear, don't get upset if you have to repeat yourself as it takes a little longer for me to process things. I'm not deaf, you do not have to yell, I still have my intuition that "gut feeling" that for some reason I did not lose. So I can tell if you're talking to me like a baby. What you are doing there is stepping on my fingers when I'm trying to get up and you are keeping me down. The greatest exercise for the human heart is to reach down and lift up another.

I may say things from time to time out of fear or anger that may hurt your feelings and make you question our friendship. This too will pass with time. Please remind me I was out of line, don't just leave me and walk away never to return. Make me aware of the hurt I have caused you in a gentle way.

I'm not crying because I feel so sorry for you, I'm crying for me. "Poor me, why me, this can't be happening to me". I want you to know this is a phase I'm going through, "me-me-me " but it I will pass as well. It is just a phase, a phase that I will need your help with. I cannot do this alone.

You'll get frustrated because I'm not the same person I was last week or last month. I have changed, give me time and I will change again for the better. Love me and encourage me, remind me of things we used to do, show me pictures.

My hope is that if I was on the receiving end of this letter I would show you kindness and compassion.

Thank you, my friends!

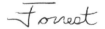

"If you have one smile in you, give it to the people you love. Don't be surly at home, then go out in the street and start grinning 'Good Morning' at total strangers."
—Maya Angelou, Poet

If I could write a letter to me and send it back in time this is what it would read.

Dear Forrest

Forrest, get up out of that bed of misery and pity that you lay in all day, you have a wonderful life and so much runway ahead of you, a beautiful wife and son that love you more than you can imagine and all you're doing is pushing them away. Stop and look around at what you're doing to yourself, it doesn't have to be this way. There are better days ahead, you just have to open your mind to see them.

When one door closes another opens, you are so focused on the door that closed you cannot see the open one.

I would suggest you get rid of all the negative influences in your life ... you know the ones. The ones you think are your friends who bathe in the same puddle of pity as you, almost as if it's a contest to see who has it worse (You think you've got it bad? Well let me tell you what happened to me last night ...).

Please say goodbye to all of your alibis, write them down and burn the paper or tear it up and flush it down the toilet never to be seen again.

I can tell you from the future that I have met hundreds of people recovering from the same injuries and I see one thing in common with people who do not succeed in their recovery and that is there is a massive list of alibis or stories about why they can't do things.

These are the exact things that are stopping these people as well as yourself from a speedy recovery.

I know it is difficult to drop or dismiss these alibis or excuses because they are part of you. After all, you are the one who thought them up, they are your little babies and you are the one who formed a habit of continually using them.

When this happens you become attached to these alibis and use them as a crutch or as excuses as to why you can't do something.

And Forrest, here is a list of some of your famous alibis. See if any sound familiar.

I forgot....
I can't read it because I have a brain injury
I can't talk on the phone because I stutter....
I can't do that because it makes me tired....
If I only had a good education.....
If only I were younger....
If only I had been given a chance....
If only I had someone to help me...
If only everybody wasn't against me...
If only I could just get a lucky break...
If only people understood me....
If only that accident didn't happen...
If only there was a magic pill to fix my brain..
If only other people would listen to me...
If only I had the courage to look in the mirror and admit to myself that I am the one, and the only one, bringing these problems on myself.

By doing that and giving up all blame and excuses, it would be the beginning of a new life and believe me when you can do that a load is lifted off your back. You'll feel better physically and emotionally. I'm only speaking to you from experience, so please give it a try and let them go. Only then can you truly begin to heal.

Go see a psychologist or therapist as soon as you can, this will help you in your progress. Don't be shy or embarrassed about it, because it turns out to be awesome.

Pay more attention to your therapists from the beginning and take an active role participating in whatever strategies they are trying to teach you. You will find out they are not around forever so accept their help now.

Don't get stressed out and make yourself sick over an upcoming neuro-psych test. It turns out they were the only tests in my life that I didn't have to study for! All you have to do is be yourself, show up and be honest.

If you're faced with an upsetting or confusing decision ask the other party if you can think about it for a day, this will stop you from making wrong impulsive decisions and save you a lot of grief and money (Remember, the quickest way to find something that is lost around the house is to go buy a replacement).

Spend more time with your son. I know you're tired and you want to sleep, so sleep on the couch with him while he is watching TV. Just spend more time with him and let him know you love him every day.

Kiss your wife every day and let her know how much she means to you. Think about the last 10 things you say before you leave the house.

Give hugs to everyone you love, and show them love as if it may be the last time see them as you know from experience that it may be.

And finally find something funny to laugh at every day and keep smiling.

PS. Stay off eBay! That Mustang convertible from Texas you want is not a wise idea ... it is an unwise impulsive idea: One. You do not have the money. Two. You don't get your license back for another two years. Three. You will save a lot of frustration for your wife and she will not have to explain why you cannot follow through with this deal.

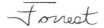

Baseballs Don't Bounce

"The people who get on in this world are the
people who get up and look for the
circumstances they want,
and if they can't find them they make them."
—George Bernard Shaw, Playwright,
Nobel Prize for literature winner

Hoarders

If you have not seen the hit television show hoarders you probably know someone who has; it is a show based on people's problems in hoarding useless junk. When you listen to the people's stories they all start the same way ... collecting an item here and then an item there and soon they are overwhelmed. It seems like there is no help for them because their lives are taken over by this clutter and it becomes all-consuming. Eventually they need an intervention from friends and family and also some professional help. Hoarding is an empty fulfillment. There is nothing there, but it makes them feel good for some reason.

I didn't notice this in myself until I had seen the show a few times. Wow, me a hoarder? I can say now I was a hoarder, not in the sense that you think, collecting junk in my house and around my yard. No, it was much worse. I was a mental hoarder, collecting and hanging onto all sorts of junk in my mind, negative thoughts and emotions. (Oh no, I'm going to be late for my doctor's appointment, I wish this damn traffic would hurry up, I forgot to call Gary back, nothing works out for me, something bad has to happen soon, things have been going too good for too long.) We've all had days like this, but when every minute of every day is filled with thoughts like these your mind is packed full just like the old closet you open only to find it is packed from floor to ceiling with unmarked boxes. One of those boxes contains a receipt and you need to return an item. It is very hard to sort through the clutter and very frustrating when you think about it, so it is much easier just to give up, isn't it?

I did not know at the time how harmful this was to myself, my family and most of all my recovery. With the help of Dr. Davidson I found that having a clear mind was a major step towards recovery, not only with my mental health but with my relationships. He showed me that I could slow down, clear my mind of all thoughts except a few important ones and that I would see the world a lot clearer and be a lot less stressed and negative. I am very excited to say that he was very right, which makes me and my family very happy!

This is where I learned to use the three D's: **Do it, Delegate it or Dump it.**

Dr. Davidson shared a lot of wisdom with me that made a lot of sense. I soon learned that not everybody can do everything but everybody can do something.

So if you're thinking of something that has to be done, don't just keep it in your memory bank or on the back burner; you either do it right away and get it out of the way or delegate it to someone who can do it. Don't be afraid to ask for help. You will be surprised at how many people are willing to help you.

The final thing you can do is dump it. Get it right out of your mind if it is not important. Just throw it in the trash bin and forget it - that's the one I had the biggest problem with, all these little things of very little importance were taking up space and cluttering my brain and my thoughts and keeping me on an emotional roller coaster.

My hope is that if you are an emotional or mental hoarder you will seek some help and learn to clear the clutter that is holding you back on your road to recovery.

And if you have not seen the show 'Hoarders', take the time to watch it once and see the similarities between yourself and the people on the show. See the positive changes it has made in their lives once the clutter is gone and how great they feel. It is like they have been given a second chance in life. You too can experience this just by getting rid of the clutter - it is very simple.

I did not say easy, I said simple.

"A lot of people have ideas, but there are few who decide to do something about them now. Not tomorrow. Not next week. But today. The true entrepreneur is a doer, not a dreamer."—Nolan Bushnell, Founder of Atari Computer

Understanding

Understanding the grieving process and the feelings that accompany those stages.

If in the beginning you can understand the stages of grieving that a person with a brain injury may go through it can make everyone's life a little easier and remove some of the wonder and questions you may be having about what is going on.

Denial *(not the river in Africa)*

When I look back now and talk about it with my wife I was probably in denial for well over a year but probably closer to two. Denial is a term used to describe the tendency to minimize undesirable personal characteristics, behaviours or events that have happened in your life. You may try to do everything you did before and say things like "there's nothing wrong with me, I'm fine." Those are words I have said many times. In the dictionary denial is described as a refusal to grant the truth of the statement or allegation.

Contradiction

This is an unconscious defence mechanism characterized by a refusal to acknowledge painful realities, thoughts or feelings.

In my world it meant sweeping my problems under the rug or just hoping if I held out long enough all my troubles would go away. "Don't worry, just give me a few weeks and I'll be back to normal" or "I'm just going through a phase" and "Not me, I'm not brain injured, that is just a term the doctors use," were common comments that I have made many times. All in hopes that I really was going through a phase and that things would be good in a few weeks. But if you're not careful those weeks turn into months and then years.

I had no idea that denial was preventing me from recognizing and dealing with the problems I was having and was only postponing my journey to recovery. For the longest time I would not change my focus, I would just deny that there was a problem. Eventually that damn of problems I kept holding back finally blew up in my face and it felt like I was drowning.

The quicker you can get out of that denial stage the sooner you can begin to recover. Look in the mirror and say to yourself, "I have a brain injury and I will work as well as I can to recover as soon as I can".

If you can't admit it to yourself, how can you admit it to others who are able to help you? If you say "I'm fine, it's ok," why would people help you?

Anger

Why me? I was angry with everyone that came into contact with me whether they knew it or not. And this was for many different reasons that didn't really make a lot of sense when I look back now. I think the number one reason I was angry with people, was that they didn't understand what I was going through. I was angry with myself for not being able to understand what was going on inside of me.

Bargaining

I remember thinking "I would give everything I own just to have the old 'me' back".

You also may find yourself bargaining when it is too late. For example, if your relationship with someone has gone sour you may find yourself saying things like "I will get some help and stop my angry outbursts if you just stay." Most of the time when you get to that point it is too late. So remember this: be kind to your partners, friends and family members. They too can only handle so much before they reach their breaking point.

Guilt

Guilt was explained to me by one of my doctors as the feeling you get when you violate your own standards. You may feel that you've done something wrong and inside you know you want to fix it. You may also feel regretful for something you have done or something that has happened in your past.

You may feel guilty for many reasons ... maybe you survived a car accident and the other person didn't. I have met people going through this exact problem. One person I know gets very angry when someone talks about his accident where he was left brain-injured and in a wheelchair and knowing that his best friend was killed. He carries the guilt around like a one-hundred pound sack of rocks; you can tell that it is just dragging him down. But he does not want to talk about that guilt. I believe it is because he is still in the denial stage.

You may feel guilty being at home and not at work during your recovery while your husband or wife is working just to keep the bills paid. I felt guilty for many reasons. I couldn't even read my son a night-time story. "What kind of father am I?" I would ask myself. But should I have felt guilty? Knowing that I couldn't even read the directions on the back of a box of Kraft Dinner at that time, no... I should not have felt guilty.

But I did.

Depression

This is one of the stages which I believe destroys more people than you can imagine. Once you realize that you are not the same person you were, you may give up all hope on your future. "It's no use so why even try?" You may have feelings such as hopelessness, being overloaded or overwhelmed, sad or blue.

You may start to neglect yourself, for example not brushing your teeth or hair, wearing the same clothes for days on end or even not eating. Or you may go the opposite way and begin overeating, because eating is the easiest way to change the way you feel. For some people it is the use of drugs or alcohol but for most it is eating. Just look around at people you know. Do you know someone who does not feel good about theirself? Someone who is overweight from constant snacking or overindulging in comfort foods? That food may be the only thing that makes them feel good.

If you or someone you know is suffering from depression, please reach out and help them or let them help you.

Fear

Fear is a feeling of agitation and anxiety caused by the presence or imminence of danger. Concern that you are in danger or think you are in danger.

Fantasized-**E**vents-**A**ppearing-**R**eal

That is how my doctor described my fear of being a passenger in a car - I was terrified and would scream and grab the dash as if I was about to be in an accident all over again. All I could think of while riding in the car was that it was going to happen again, it was just a matter of time. I was literally making myself sick from the fear and anxiety I had of riding in a car or thinking something bad was going to happen soon.

After a lot of counselling I realized that my fear was just that: a fantasized event appearing real. In my head I knew it was just going to happen again. It's been nine years now and it very rarely happens anymore.

I want to share with you that ninety-nine percent of the things I feared did not happen at all and the one percent that did were not nearly as bad as I thought they were.

Acceptance

This is the final stage of grieving, and the one you should be working towards as soon as possible.

This is when you begin to realize that people admire you for your strength, courage and wisdom.

This is when I began to accept who I am and not who I used to be.

This is when I took the focus off my brain injury and stopped living with the victim mentality of "oh poor me" and decided I was going to be a survivor, and the best one I could be.

This is when miracles happen. This is a time to look forward to and be excited about. This is the time for you to look at the choices you have.

This is a time to forgive, and for me being able to forgive the person that was driving the car that day relieved me of a lot of pain and anger I had been holding for quite some time. I realized you cannot move forward if you are always looking back, you must let go of the past to embrace the future.

I began to let go of the pains and focused on the gains that could be achieved without all this emotional baggage weighing me down.

This is when I stopped caring what society thought 'brain-injured' meant, and realized that having an uninjured brain was not the secret to happiness.

I had that secret with me all along. It was all in my head.

The art of acceptance is the art of making someone who has just done you a small favor wish that he might have done you a greater one.
—Russell Lynes

"To be yourself in a world that is constantly trying to make you something else is the greatest accomplishment."
—Ralph Waldo Emerson, Poet and Essayist

The Iceberg Effect

Don't become an iceberg. I was one myself. For years I showed a fake smile and a nod just as if everything was okay. But what people did not know was that just under the water beneath that little smile was a huge iceberg of pain, confusion, anger, depression and anxiety to name a few.

If I met people I knew but could not remember their names I would try to fumble my way through it with a smile, nodding my head as if I knew what they were talking about, while inside I was having an anxiety attack trying to remember their name.

I was too embarrassed to ask them their name; they obviously knew me very well ... they were talking to me about things in my past and asking how my family is.

How dare I insult these people by saying "I don't remember your name" was the thought that went through my head.

And then I accepted some help from Dr. Davidson who helped me accept me for who I was and what I was going through. He shared with me that avoidance was the problem, not the solution. And that as I was hiding behind these little riddles of guessing names and events, my iceberg was getting bigger and I was on course to sink a ship - my own ship.

The first time I was able to bring myself to admit to a person "I'm sorry I don't remember your name right now I'm just recovering from a brain injury I acquired in a car accident, I know that I know you but your name is just not clicking right now," I felt the weight of the world lifted from my shoulders. It actually felt good to get that out. I thought to myself nothing bad happened ... the person didn't look at me as if I was an alien ... and all the negative thoughts in my head were simply not true.

As time went on and I was able to explain to everyone I knew what I was going through, the more support I was given from everyone around me was amazing. And with that support, it gave me encouragement to carry on with my recovery in a positive atmosphere knowing that everyone was behind me and not against me.

So if you feel like an iceberg, reach out and get some help.

A Random Thought

We are all in the Same Classroom

It doesn't matter who you are or where you are from... how much money you have, or don't have...what school or college you went to... what sex you are or the colour of your skin. Brain injury does not discriminate, whether you're sixty-two or twenty-eight.

Because with an acquired brain injury we are all equal, we are all in the same class-room now re-learning to cope with life. That's right, I said re-learning. All of the intelligence is still in your head, it's a jigsaw puzzle that fell on the floor. You just have to put the pieces back together. Everything is still all there, you just have to work on putting it back together. Sometimes a piece of your puzzle gets kicked under the couch and it takes a little longer to find it but don't give up. It's there. Or like a groundhog frightened into its hole by a lawnmower, eventually it will have to come out ... or live a life in a cold dark place. You must also learn to come out into the sunshine by removing your fears and anxieties to take a chance and live a great life.

"The best job goes to the person who can
get it done without passing the buck
or coming back with excuses."
—Napoleon Hill, Author of
"Think and Grow Rich"

Join a Support Group Today

"I believe in angels because
my angels believe in me"

My angels are all the beautiful people I have met over the years at support groups that I have attended. Getting me to join a support group was very difficult as I was still in the denial stage. "There's nothing wrong with me, I don't need to go to a support group," were the statements I would often make, but the truth was I needed it more than I knew and looking back I wish I would've joined years earlier. Just to make things clear, a support group can be made up of professionals or volunteers who have a keen interest in the well-being of people with acquired brain injury, as well as the people who have acquired brain injuries themselves. I would not consider a bunch of guys sitting around your neighbour's garage drinking beer and solving the world's problems to be your support group. They do not have the knowledge to solve some of the problems that may occur on your journey to recovery. They may tell you what to do if they were in your shoes, but they are not in your shoes and remember the only good thing about free advice is its price.

No one will know what you are going through on your journey to recovery except you and the others at the support group. No one will experience the extreme emotions of success, failure and setbacks on your road to recovery other than the people at the support groups because like yourself they are driven to fulfill their dreams of recovery. They also have your best interests in mind and are always willing to help you with your goals.

And like you, they dream of better days ahead.

The first time I went to a support group meeting was a few years after my accident. It was run by the March of Dimes and recommended to me by my speech therapist Christine. I was dropped off by a taxicab at our local Legion. As I grabbed the door handle to enter I was paralyzed with fear knowing that I was stepping out of my comfort zone and the safety of my own home. I wanted to puke, my hands and knees were shaking and I was sweating bullets. I felt flooded by the waves of anxiety washing over me. But somehow I mustered up the courage to go in and face the music. " What the hell," I said , "let's get this over with so I can tell Christine that I went, then I can leave after five minutes." Bailing out and running from my fears as I usually do.

I felt very uncomfortable at the meeting, feeling very tense and uneasy from the anxiety of the unknown. "What are they going to ask me? What if I can't speak properly? What if I screw up, are they going to laugh at me?" All these negative thoughts went through my head that day. And when I left the meeting? I felt as if a huge weight was lifted from my shoulders and the elephant that was standing on my chest (anxiety) was gone and my breathing slowed down.

All those negative thoughts were gone. I felt great about myself. Finally I had found a place where I felt comfortable with who I was and with my disabilities and abilities. It was also a huge relief to realize that I was not alone. Lori Wood with the March of Dimes introduced me to all of the people and made me feel welcome and comfortable and I am forever grateful to her for that day and every day and I continue to go to the support groups and help others who have a lot of the same feelings I did.

I would also like to thank Sorina Henry from the March of Dimes for her continual support and encouragement not to give up on finishing this book.

"I don't know of any other characteristic more important to achieving success than persistence. Never has there been a time when this incredible virtue has failed to create greatness in the person whose heart and soul has been gallantly given in pursuit of a dream."
—John Assaraf, Author

Why me? Why, Why, Why?

That is the question I have asked myself many times over and I still don't have the answer for. I now realize that I can better spend my time thinking about the future and not dwelling on the past and looking forward to the great things to come. I also realized that I must let go of the past to embrace the future. The answer to the question 'Why me?' may never be answered.

I've had people say to me in the past that it was unfortunate what had happened and all the terrible things I had to go through over the last nine years. I think it would be unfortunate if things didn't happen the way they did because then I would not have met all these wonderful people and been able to help others in ways I never thought possible and finally find true happiness in life.

I am in a much better place now than I was before the accident. I am truly living a happy fulfilling life surrounded by wonderful people and making great changes in the world one person at a time. It is hard to explain the feeling I get in seeing a person I have met who thought at one time, "this is it. There's no hope for me." And who now is making leaps and bounds in their recovery and is excited about what the future holds. To me that is more exciting and fulfilling than chasing the almighty dollar in a rat race job like I did for so many years. If this incident did not happen to me I would not have known what it is like to truly be happy and enjoy life everyday.

Here are a few other questions in life that I probably won't find the answer to:

Why do I push the buttons on the remote harder when I know the batteries are getting weak?

How come you never hear father- in-law jokes?

"When designing our future we should always ask these questions: Why? Why not? Why not me? Why not now!"
—Jim Rohn

Where's your Daddy?

When a child loses a parent to acquired brain injury there is no pharmaceutical company or doctor's prescription that can bring that bond back; it takes time and love.

About eight months after the accident Julie wanted to go shopping for a few hours with one of her friends but there was no one to watch our son Hunter. I could not drive, take care of the household bills or even use the stove safely at this point. Surely the one thing I was capable of doing was to watch my own son for a few hours, how hard could it be? Put Bob the Builder in the VCR and lay on the couch for a few hours, right? Wrong. Hunter fell asleep on the couch and I went out to the garage - I don't remember what for - but my brother pulled in the driveway stating he was going to the hardware store and asked if I would like to go for a drive. I said sure and jumped in his truck and off we went to town. We returned about an hour later still not thinking anything was wrong until we pulled down the driveway and I saw some cars in the driveway. That's when I got a rude awakening.

There are only so many toothless grins and
chances to be a Superhero to your children.
Enjoy them while you can.

Hunter had woken up after I left and my neighbour heard him crying and saw him with his arms raised pushing on the glass door so she immediately ran over to find out what was going on. The house was empty so she thought something was wrong and called other neighbours to look for myself and Julie. Everyone was in panic mode and I pulled down the driveway like everything was fine until I got out of the truck.

Over the next few days I was given many talks and interventions from my family, doctors and therapists and after getting everything straightened out there were no charges for child neglect but that may have been easier to accept than what was to come ... no, not the wraith of my mother- in-law ... it was worse. It was determined that I was not fit to keep my own son by myself. In fact the powers that be determined I was not fit to keep myself with myself at this time so what followed was 24 hours attentive care until I could prove I would be safe on my own. They called it attentive care. I called it a babysitter.

Just one mistake can change your whole life in a short time. I wish I could take that day back and I do regret it. This is a very personal and embarrassing thing for me to admit. I just hope this story can serve as a lesson to people to focus on what you are doing and be realistic about what you are capable of. You can see that the one thing I thought I could handle turned out to be my biggest mistake. Although this was a big wake up call it wasn't enough for me to make a huge change in my life. That wouldn't happen for another two years when I discovered that baseball's don't bounce.

"To bring up a child in the way he should go, travel that way yourself once in a while."
—*Josh Billings*

Baseballs Don't Bounce

There's an old Chinese proverb that says "fall down seven times and get up eight." If your journey is anything like mine you will fall down many times. The important thing is to keep getting up.

Someone once said to me "you've got to roll with the punches". Well sometimes that gets very hard because you ask yourself, when are the punches going to stop coming? Let me tell you they don't, not for a long time. As you can imagine things were not very good in the first few years and my future was looking very unclear.

Looking back now I can see that I could have reduced a lot of stress on myself and my family and I could have excelled in my recovery if we had only known ahead of time some of the obstacles we were going to face. The big turnaround in my life and the way I looked at things and dealt with my problems happened just over 2 1/2 years after my accident at my son's fifth birthday party.

I was sitting on a chair in the distance as

always, because a bunch of kids laughing and yelling would rattle my nerves to no end.

Someone had bought my son a baseball glove and ball. When he opened it he dropped the ball several times looking at the ground and one of his friends shouted, "Baseballs don't bounce!" Those three simple words hit me harder than a punch in the stomach. "Baseballs don't bounce".

I couldn't believe how overcome with emotion I became, I had to go into the house because I broke down crying. It was then I realized how selfish I had become. I was so consumed with my own problems and self-pity that I was neglecting the things that were most important in my life ... my family. I realized my son was now five and I had not yet taught him how to skate or even catch a ball.

It was then that I made the decision to give up all excuses and start rebuilding my life, giving an effort of 100% not only to my recovery but to my family and myself.

There are little signs and signals out there that are trying to get your attention every day and lucky for me I got this one! This time.

It was a very emotionally troubling time for me

as I was just deemed catastrophic by the Glasgow outcome scale which means I had a permanent loss of 55% or more of myself as a whole person based on Neuro- cognitive/mental and behavioral disorders. The doctors also had in their report that I had plateaued. That means I had reached 95 to 98% of the spontaneous recovery that I could expect.

I don't believe the doctors were on the same mountain as me because I don't believe I had plateaued ... I was just beginning my climb! And oh what a tough climb it would be. I am still recovering nine years later and I imagine I will continue recovering for the rest of my life. I can also say that it gets easier as time passes. Please don't wait for two and half or three years to go by before you realize that "baseballs don't bounce" or whatever your signal or wake-up call in life may be to come along and kick you in the pants because it may be too late. Lucky for me my family was still there after all that time. You may not be so lucky so try to make a change for the better today.

Don't wait.

You Matter

Chances are if you're reading this book you are old enough to realize that your childhood beliefs about Santa Claus and the monster under your bed have changed. When I was nine I took the legs off my bed; that way I knew nothing could get under there. As you age, you no longer believe in something that cannot be proven, but the beliefs about yourself should not change just because you have gone through changes.

You must still believe that you do matter to yourself and to your family. You must look into yourself, not outside of yourself and find that you do matter. Some of the things you should do are...

- Accept yourself
- Believe in yourself
- Forgive yourself
- Compliment yourself
- Reward yourself
- Discover yourself
- Acknowledge yourself

Once you begin to do these things for yourself you'll begin to see that everything in your life becomes a little easier instead of being a struggle. You really cannot take care of anything without taking care of yourself; it all starts with you. This concept took me a few years to adapt to and when I did I noticed life became easier for myself and others around me. So start today by doing something for yourself even if it is something silly like looking in the mirror and giving yourself a wink saying, "You sure look great today!" And then laugh.

"As you grow older, you'll find the only things you regret are the things you didn't do."
—Zachary Scott, Actor

Fatigue, Stress and Worry

These three things can consume you if you don't get them under control quickly. They feed off each other and multiply so fast that they will lead you down a dark and lonely path were you don't want to be. I know. I've been down that path many times. I was not able to focus because I was always too tired from worrying about things that for the most part didn't exist. I was even worrying because of times I wasn't worrying. I thought, "Something's up, things are going too good today, something bad has to happen to me soon."

Have you ever had times when you forgot what you were doing, thinking or talking about? Where you sometimes forgot even where you were? The names of familiar things slip your mind. You are talking and forget what you are talking about halfway through the sentence. Words come out of your mouth that you didn't mean to say or that have nothing to do with what you're talking about. These all may be signs of fatigue and stress.

I have learned that fatigue, stress and worry cause the same in return. It is like a hamster wheel from which you can't get off. If you notice some of these things happening, you may want to look for some help before it consumes you. These three symptoms will also produce anxiety and depression.

"Man's mind once stretched by a new idea,
never regains its original dimensions."
—Oliver Wendell Holmes, Jr. American Author

A big Salute to our Troops

I would like to thank the men and woman, young and old, of our armed forces, including my brother in-law Cpl James Briggs with over twenty years of service, for risking their lives to save ours. The sad fact is that head injury is the number one injury of our troops returning from war.

Left to right: Forrest WIllet, Pte Jennifer Ellis and Pte JP Carbonneau

I believe there should be more awareness made to the public and more services available for the men and woman who serve us. It would be the least we could do.

Recently I had the good fortune to meet with Private Jennifer Ellis second field ambulance and Private J.P. Carbonneau second field ambulance, (pictured above). They are two of the many people who are saving the wounded soldiers who protect all of us.

Thank you.

I cannot relate to what it would feel like to be in combat, but I can relate to the effects of a traumatic experience and its effects including Post-Traumatic Stress Disorder. This can be a very disabling disorder changing your life forever, one big problem with it is people cannot see it, it is an invisible disability you may look good on the outside yet your falling apart on the inside. This problem is also common among police and firefighters. I believe our government should be doing more for these people to get them back on their feet instead of spending millions of dollars repaving roads that are fine, spend some money rehabilitating our people who put their lives at risk each day so we can walk around feeling safe. This is not a new problem it has been around for years my good friend Tim Nesbitt was in World War Two and has seen the effects of PTSD back then and how it has changed people's lives and not in a good way.

I first met Tim where he lives and I volunteer at the Villa retirement lodge, we have since became close friends we have a lot in common, we both love chicken wings that is what we order

My good friend, Tim Nesbitt

when we go for lunch and we were both born on the same week in March just fifty years apart. When I told Tim about writing a part in the book about PTSD he was kind enough to open up and share a story with me.

He told me that when he first arrived in Normandy in June of 1944 he was 23 years old, he went to an air base in Sainte-Croix-sur-Mer. He was with the 443 squadron did not get in until late in the night. Most of the fellows were under ground so he took cover with another guy under the back of a big truck to shelter themselves from the shelling. He thought to himself, 'if one of those shells hits the truck I'm a goner'.

When morning came he heard bagpipes, so he went for a walk to investigate the noise that was coming from a British field hospital. What Tim saw there will stay with him for the rest of his life. There were three commandos brutally injured with life threatening injuries, it was very troubling to see.

When Tim came back to Canada he was sent to see a psychologist she asked him if he felt he had post traumatic stress and he replied no at the time now he would change his answer to yes. When she checked him out she just tested his mind and said that he was ok, what she couldn't see was the emotional wounds brought home by himself and his fellow soldiers.

It wasn't until years later that he realized the magnitude of the problem, Tim was at the Roy Thompson hall in Toronto to see a show with a brass band and bagpipes once the bagpipes started he was overcome with emotion all of the bad memories of being oversees flooded him and he had to leave later that day he was hospitalized with a heart attack which the doctors believe was brought on by stress.

I thank Tim for sharing his story to help others and most of all for being a good friend to me and my son.

Post-Traumatic Stress Disorder (PTSD)

What can bring it on?

War

Car or plane crashes

Terrorist attacks

Sudden death of a loved one

Kidnapping

Assault

Common symptoms—

Anger and irritability

Guilt, shame or self blame

Substance abuse

Feelings of mistrust or betrayal

Feeling alienated and alone

Physical aches and pains

Depression and hopelessness

Suicidal thoughts and feelings

Baseballs Don't Bounce

This story shall the good man teach his son...
But we in it shall be remembered, we few, we
happy few, we band of brothers; for he that
sheds his blood with me shall be my brother...
—William Shakespeare

Why Does it Feel so Dirty

Why does it feel so dirty coming clean about depression?

A few years ago there was outbreak called H1N1, also known as the swine flu. I received a call from my doctor's office asking me if I would like to be vaccinated. After thinking about it for a while I realized that no one had ever phoned me to warn me about emotional sicknesses such as depression, anxiety and stress. Why would that be? Emotional sickness causes ten thousand times more damage and kills more people than the swine flu, yet it is something that people rarely talk about. I hope that this section of the book will help to rid you of of some of your stress and worry.

Even as I'm writing this, it feels very odd letting the world in on my dirty little secret of depression, when just a few short years ago I would not even admit it to myself. I thought that if I admit to myself or accept the fact that I was depressed people would think of me differently like I'm some kind of weirdo or less of a person in some ways. I guess I hoped it would just go away on its own.

How can he be depressed? He's always smiling and joking.

If people only knew how hard it was to wear that fake smile every day and pretend to be a trooper. "Don't worry about me I'm getting along just fine, everything is great." That was on the outside.

On the inside it was a totally different story. "I am worried about me; I don't how much longer I can keep this up."

The stress and anxiety was overwhelming in trying to keep up with this "everything-is-super" attitude. It was not only mental it was very much physical. I often found myself at the doctor's office with many different symptoms, most of which I later found out were related to my depression, stress and anxiety. Here is a list of the common symptoms I had complained to the doctor about:

- Feeling dizzy and lightheaded
- Sweaty palms and under-arms
- Tightness in the chest as if I was having a heart attack

- Feeling unsteady, shaky knees
- Dry mouth
- Sore neck and tense neck muscles
- A racing heart like I had just run a race and yet I was sitting on the couch
- Butterflies in my stomach
- Diarrhea "I should have bought shares in Pepto-Bismol!"
- Frequent urination
- Difficulty concentrating on one thing with my mind racing
- Difficulty sleeping
- Difficulty paying attention

These are just some of the symptoms I had. I could go on and on but as I talk with others these symptoms seem to be common with many people going through the same thing. My family doctor made a few suggestions. The first was plain old exercise which turned out to be one of the greatest weapons in this war. Walking daily does relieve stress and makes you feel better.

Another suggestion of his was to see a psychologist to get some help because I was about to crash and crash hard.

On the outside I was a big strong guy making an excellent comeback from tragedy and on the inside I was a five-year-old kid separated from my family in a busy mall not knowing where to turn, crying for someone to help me find my way.

Along comes Dr. Thomas Davidson into my life. Before I met him he was the last person in the world I wanted to see and I didn't even know him. The reason I didn't want to see him was that I thought I could hang on to the last piece of my self-dignity. Getting me to go see a psychologist was like giving a cat a bath, it was very difficult. "I don't need to go see some quack and lay on a couch going over all my problems; there is nothing wrong with me, just leave me alone". I was still in denial.

The fact is he helped me with my self dignity and self esteem. We all have pictures in our head of what a psychologist looks like or acts like by what you see in the movies. The old white-haired guy with round glasses smoking a pipe and driving an old Volvo station wagon. When I first met Dr. Davidson, I can say I had my guard up almost as if he was a mind reader who was going to take my brain out and dissect it. Well, he didn't. I was surprised. He was a cool, laid-back guy, very friendly, one of those people who are just very likeable.

Now that my concerns are eased and my guard has been lowered we can get to work. I won't bore you with the small talk, but what I learned from him can help you overcome one of the biggest obstacles you will face. He showed me that fatigue, stress and worry cannot exist in the presence of complete relaxation. You cannot continue to worry if you relax. So to prevent fatigue, stress and worry, you must learn to rest often. Rest before you get tired. What do you have to lose?

Sounds odd but it works. So I started to rest every day, putting it in my day timer slots as if it was an important meeting, and it was.

An important meeting with myself that helped me greatly with my recovery. You can do it anywhere and at any time.

Here are a few examples of relaxation.

Lie down on the floor or couch for ten to fifteen minutes and close your eyes. You don't have to fall into a deep sleep, just turn you head off like a light switch. Imagine you are on a cloud just floating around. Let yourself relax completely. All of your muscles are at ease. Remember, a tense muscle is a working muscle; you are not working here. Relax, you can do this anywhere. At work, during lunch or when at home. I often do it right in the airport before I get on the plane. Do people think I'm different? I don't care because it is none of my business what others think of me. I'm relaxed and they are not.

Sit in a chair or car seat and focus on a spot on the dash (not if you're driving) or a spot on the floor and stare at it for a minute then close your eyes for a couple of minutes. When you open your eyes, look again at the spot where you were concentrating and focus only on that spot. All of your other worries go on vacation for a short while and you can relax. It really works. I didn't cure my fatigue. I didn't have to cure it. I prevented it.

"Don't just do something, stand there". That's right, just stand there at times or sit down and have some time to yourself. Whether it is two minutes or two hours, just do nothing. My problem was trying to be everything for everybody just to prove there was nothing wrong with me. The problem was I burned myself out trying to prove that I could still do things when I should've been resting. I now realize that your body heals when it is resting. You must do things in life and take on new tasks and try different things but you must also take time to relax. Relaxation really helped me with my depression and sleep disorder, pain and anxiety, and also helped to sharpen my concentration.

Because I rested frequently, I was able to work on my recovery fresh and fit.

You owe it to yourself to just give it a try; if you don't take the time to relax you could have trouble at home or at work and get wiped out emotionally and physically. Suddenly it seems possible that all your efforts might be for nothing and that's not a good feeling, so just relax and watch your worries disappear; it costs nothing to try.

Fatigue or lack of sleep would turn out to be one of my biggest problems from day one. It starts in the hospital. Every hour on the hour they are waking you up and checking your vital signs, poking and prodding your body. People are constantly in your room so it is very hard to get any rest unless of course they drug you, which they obviously did to me. While in my hospital stay I was given a morphine pump and I was allowed to give myself a dose with the pump on my intravenous line. My wife said that I would press it constantly hoping to feel better as I dosed in and out of consciousness. And poor sleep continued to be a problem when I returned home because there were now many more distractions to deal with.

Practice 'prepared calm'. My neighbour is a commercial airline pilot and I have talked to him about dealing with stress. How do you keep it together if something bad were to go wrong in the air? His reply was they practice prepared calm; every few months they are tested in a simulator and given every possible negative situation that could occur such as engine failure, loss of cabin pressure or a violent passenger. Once they are subjected to these situations they are now prepared to deal with them in a calm and cool manner; they know how to handle the situation.

What a great idea! After our talk I started to review a lot of negative thoughts I was having and to think how I would handle each situation if it were to occur. This really set my mind at ease now that I was prepared for anything that was thrown my way. I suggest you try it.

These are my weapons in
The War on Depression.
What are yours?

Tattoos and Suicide

Tattoos and suicide are two things I would highly recommend you avoid at all costs.

Suicide is the subject that people don't want to talk about so I thought I would break the ice with tattoos. You see the two of them have a lot in common. I know people who have gotten tattoos and people who have attempted suicide and every one of them regret their decision. When I talk to people about those things they all seemed to have been done on an impulsive emotional thought about someone or something and they were carried out (or attempted) without putting much thought to the final outcome and to their future. And I believe both of them are done as a cry for help or attention in some way.

Suicide is a subject that must be talked about. There have been many people right here in my little town that have taken their own lives just in this past year and most of them are men. I also believe that if these people had someone to talk with about their problems these situations could have been avoided. Suicide is a permanent solution to temporary problems.

As I am writing this today a police officer in our town just took his own life and it has devastated not only his family and co-workers who my heart goes out to, but it has shaken the whole community.

I have been fortunate enough to meet a great person who has attempted suicide. The good thing is he is still with us and he shares his story with others in attempting to help others avoid the same situation. This person attempted suicide after an acquired brain injury he received when he fell down a flight of stairs. He also suffered from severe depression, another subject that should be talked about without shame.

This man is a very intelligent person, far more educated than I. I mean this is the kind of guy who could teach my chemistry teacher about chemistry. After his brain injury he became very depressed because he could no longer do his job and what he loved. He lost his job at the lab.

From there he felt life as he knew it was over. How could this man, a modern-day Albert Einstein, come to such a conclusion? I didn't know so I asked him what had happened. What was the straw that broke the camel's back? He said he became so depressed and frustrated that he could no longer do his job. He felt worthless and he also felt he was a burden on his family so he decided everyone would be better off without him. So one day, as he tells me of his first suicide attempt, he phoned the local hospital and told them that he took in a large quantity of pills. He was taken to the hospital were he had his stomach pumped out.

The next Saturday he phoned the local hospital saying that he had suicidal thoughts and they told him to call back on Monday when he could talk to a counselor (I'm not making this up). Take into account that this happened years ago before they had suicide hotlines and 24-hour counselors.

So anyway he stabbed himself in the heart and slashed his wrists (I have seen the scars and they are scary). He was flown to a Toronto hospital by air ambulance and pronounced dead in the air and was once again revived.

He went on to tell me that what he did not realize was that "hell" was waiting for him just around the corner and by that he did not mean death- it was worse, he explained. Worse than the pain and depression that he suffered in the past? What could be worse?

He spent the next 60 days in a mental institution where he was subjected to electric shock therapy and enough drugs to make a zombie out of an elephant. If you thought it was hard to look for a job before just put that on your resume now … no, wait a minute … he didn't have to because when you live in a small town like us everyone knows what happened and it usually gets blown way out of proportion.

After all of this he still suffers from depression but has it under control with proper medication. He is also in the middle of putting what he knows best on paper, writing a massive book about the medicinal uses of exotic plants. I see him on a regular basis and I am proud to call him a friend. He is also an inspiration to the many people he shares his story with.

If you know anyone who is sending out a cry for help please reach out and help them; just talking to someone over a cup of coffee can mean the difference between life and death. People want to be heard and to share their stories.

Enough about the sad talk! Let's have some fun and get back to the tattoos. I know a guy in his sixties who had a grim reaper tattooed on his chest when he was in his twenties. Now that he has aged and his body is not as fit as it once was that grim reaper looks like Yoda from Star Wars. A friend of ours had a Chinese symbol tattooed on her arm. She said it means peace and love but she does not read Chinese so for all she knows it could say 'number seven with an egg roll'.

My youngest brother had a tattoo put on in remembrance of his best friend who died of a brain injury sustained in a car accident. This is a perfect example of making a decision on an emotional impulse without much thought for the future or the consequences. He has been embarrassed about it for years, always covering it up and is now looking into having it removed.

He also has to explain to his four year- old son why he has those marks on his body.

My advice would be if you are thinking of a tattoo get a fake one for a few weeks and see if you still think it is cool.

"When one door closes another door opens; but so often we look so long and regretfully upon the closed door, that we do not see the ones which open for us."
—*Alexander Graham Bell, Inventor of the telephone*

Self-Esteem

What is self-esteem?

It's simply what you think of yourself. People with high self-esteem believe in their hearts that they deserve to be happy, that they have the right to stand up for their needs. They trust in their abilities to deal with problems that come up in life.

People who have low self-esteem on the other hand, believe that they don't have the right or even the ability to stand up for themselves, although I did learn something from having low self esteem and that is there are cracks in the foundation everywhere you go no one is perfect. When you hang your head low for so long you can see imperfections everywhere even in multi billion dollar airports like Toronto, Ontario or Phoenix, Arizona they look beautiful at a glance but take a look at the beautiful granite floors there are cracks everywhere, when I see that I am reminded that we all have little cracks in our foundation.

How can you raise self-esteem?

What you need to do is to take certain actions that will give you an almost instant boost. In putting into practice the following suggestions, you will gain a clearer sense of who you are and this will boost your self-esteem.

Six ways to raise your self-esteem

1. Don't deny or lie about a problem (even to yourself). Whenever you are confronted with a problem in life, no matter how unpleasant, rather than burying your head in the sand, confront the problem head on. Admit the truth, no matter how painful it may be, and search for ways to solve the problem. There is a way.

2. Get up and do something. The person who lays in bed or on the couch everyday never feels as good about himself or herself as someone who is always participating in things. Human beings were not meant to

vegetate. We were meant to engage in goal-oriented behaviour. So start with small things, for example, get up and clean the house. Answer the mail. Make that annoying phone call to check on something you ordered. When you accomplish something, you feel much better about yourself than when you sit and do nothing.

3. Succeed in something, no matter how small. The feeling of being successful and capable builds self-esteem. When you take on a challenge and overcome it, you feel better about yourself. Start with a small success that would help you in your daily life, for example, I know so many people who hunt and peck away at the computer keyboard when a simple typing course would have them speeding away. How great these people would feel if they called their local business school and took a course. Soon they would have accomplished something that would remind them on a daily basis how

it made their life run more smoothly, that they had taken action. I did this myself Christine started me out with Mavis Beacon typing on the computer and before long I was doing well and feeling great about myself.

4. Absolutely, positively change your negative thinking. When you make a mistake in front of people, do you put yourself down? Maybe this habit started when you were a child, and your parents called you dummy every time you made a mistake. Every time you catch yourself saying something like, "Stupid. What's wrong with you?" Instead say "Whoops, I made a mistake. I guess I'm human." Believe it or not, even that simple correction will go a long way in building your self-esteem. In time, you will stop condemning yourself every time you make a mistake, and instead you will forgive yourself, and give yourself some room to be human. You learn by making mistakes.

5. Don't say "yes" when you want to say "no". This was a big one for me and I still to this day have to work on it, your self-esteem suffers when you don't assert yourself. When you go along with something because you feel too embarrassed or too intimidated to take a stand and spell out what you want. When you don't stand up for your rights, we don't want the person who's making the demand to get angry or reject us. So the next time you find yourself about to say "yes" when you really mean "no", stop dead in your tracts. Say, "no" and let the other person deal with it. Your self –esteem and sense of your own power will grow each time you do it.

6. Don't give up your dream – the key to high self-esteem. This is the most important category in building self-esteem. If you give up your dream it is very hard to have self-esteem. How can you respect yourself if you feel as if you have sold out? Never surrender the hope that you will someday be able to correct your course in life. Don't give up. If you are still striving, your self-esteem rises. You feel good about yourself because you, the most important person in your life, have not abandoned yourself.

Your chances of success in any undertaking can always be measured by your belief in yourself.
—Robert Collier

Run Forrest, Run!

No, it's o.k., I'll walk

The only exercise I was getting for quite a while were mood swings! I had a $300 clothing rack that looked a lot like an exercise bike.

It took me a long time to realize that diet and exercise are two very important solvents for the brain.

I am not talking about getting up and running a marathon. Walking is just as good for your mind and body as any other exercise. And if you cannot walk get out in your wheelchair, just get moving.

Here are some facts about walking.

• Walking improves memory. People in tests who walked on a treadmill were better at correctly identifying which numbers were repeated in a series of digits read aloud.

• Walking also improves attention, improving your ability to ignore distractions ... probably because walking activates the brain regions associated with attention.

• Biking and running may get your heart racing,

but a low intensity stroll down your street five to six times a week is actually more effective in preventing obesity and eliminating heart risk factors including high cholesterol and blood pressure.

- Walkers trim their waistlines more and shed more weight. This will also make you feel great.

Dr Coutts shared with me that if I exercised regularly it would sharpen my mind, relieve stress and improve my life overall by increasing my energy levels. At first I just shrugged it off. I wanted to learn how to speak better, read better and do simple math - those were some of my goals. Not to run a marathon or to be a star athlete. So I thought what the heck? I'll give it a try. I started walking ten to fifteen minutes before my speech therapy appointment and to my amazement in a short period of time I was making great progress.

I found that I was more alert, relaxed and able to focus on what I was doing. I felt that regular walking helped me greatly with my depression and anxiety. It lowered my tension and sadness and improved my mood overall, so much so that I was able to wean myself off the depression pills. Before you do this, please consult your Doctor. And realize that for these effects to be long term, you must maintain a regular and consistent schedule of exercise along with a good diet.

Walking regularly has also boosted my self-confidence and energy levels. After a while you will begin to see the positive results that come from regular exercise and you will feel good about yourself when you lower your daily stress level and decrease the feeling of anxieties in daily living. So the next time you feel yourself getting stressed or upset, lace up your shoes and take a walk around the block. If you are in a wheelchair, wheel yourself around the block and come home feeling refreshed.

I know it is hard to get started and easy to say "Maybe tomorrow I will start walking". But isn't it worth ten minutes of your time to start a lifetime of change? Start right now, set the book down and go for a ten minute walk and see how you feel when you get back; I'll still be here and I guarantee you'll feel great.

Walking is just one way to increase your energy levels. For the longest time I didn't realize the connection between success in recovery and my level of energy. Just for a minute stop and think about someone you know who is successful in life or who has had a successful recovery and you will probably discover that those people are full of energy; they have the energy to keep going and going even when there's obstacles in their way.

I would like to briefly go over some things you can do in life to increase your energy. I know it can be very difficult to believe you can muster up the energy to do something, especially if you're suffering from depression, laying in bed for hours a day staring at the ceiling just wishing everything would go away. That type of lifestyle drains you of your precious energy.

There are some ideas on the following pages that may help you to regain that energy and believe me, you will just have to make the effort to try some of these and see for yourself how much your life can improve.

Sleep.

I know I just said in the last paragraph that it is not good for you to lie in bed all day, but good sleep is an important part of increasing your energy. When you are sleeping you are in repair. Your mind, muscles and entire body is repairing itself while you sleep so it is very important to get a good sleep every day. Some things that may help you get some good sleep would be to keep the room dark and quiet. If you have streetlights outside your bedroom window you could hang up dark curtains or nail a blanket over the window. It is also helpful to turn off all radios and televisions because it is hard to get full rest when your brain is occupied by the noise of the television or radio. Try to get eight hours of sleep a night, it may seem impossible but you can try. Also rest during the day.

Diet.

This is very important to your energy levels. I'm not going to preach at you to become a vegetarian or eat certain foods, you can eat whatever you want. For myself I found that my energy levels would rise when I ate a lot of fruits and vegetables which in fact are far easier for your body to digest using less energy than a greasy hamburger. What usually happens after Christmas or Thanksgiving dinner? You usually see a lot of people hitting the couch because they feel drained; their bodies are using up a lot of energy to digest all that food and is all that food good for us? Turkey, mashed potatoes, gravy, stuffing, buns with butter, cakes. You get the idea and it's up to you to decide what you want to put into your energy gas tank: premium or the cheap crap.

Organization.

You may wonder as to how being organized can boost your energy and I wondered the same thing myself. I learned this simple technique from my occupational therapists Gary and Claudia. For a long time I was disorganized - I would let things slide because I didn't care about them and then I would become frustrated because I couldn't find things and that became very emotionally draining and consumed a lot of energy. Eventually they had me set up on a routine to organize and clean my house and office. Once I was able to make this a habit it was very easy to keep on top of it. It also boosted my self-esteem and energy levels by knowing where everything was located. I was no longer wasting precious time and energy looking for things. I also found that with a clear desk came a clear mind.

Lower your caffeine intake.

I used to be a coffee junkie, some days drinking 10 to 12 cups a day. Don't get me wrong, I still love coffee but I limit it to 2 to 3 cups a day and no longer drink any after 10 a.m. I also no longer drink pop or other soft drinks that contain any caffeine, especially those energy drinks (stay away). They will rob you of your energy in the long run. I can't guarantee this will work for you but I feel great and if you want to try it, it doesn't cost a thing.

"In every person that comes near you look for what is good and strong; honor that; try to imitate it, and your faults will drop off like dead leaves when their time comes."
—John Ruskin. English Philosopher

H2O

Water: The World's first energy drink

There are some facts about water that I want to bring up. I know something about water as I once worked for a water company and took every course I could about water, its properties and benefits to the human body.

Water is very important to the brain.

The average human brain is seventy to seventy-eight per cent water, so if you neglect drinking water you can imagine what it does to your brain. It would be like driving from New York to Daytona Beach on one tank of gas - eventually you'll find yourself on the side of the road wondering what happened. Drinking coffee, cola and alcohol is not the same as drinking water. Caffeine in colas and coffee actually dehydrate you. Alcohol also does the same thing, it keeps you wanting more. When you drink a cold beer on a hot day you want another and another.

So take a break in between those drinks and have a glass of water. You will feel better and it will cost you less money.

Water facts.

Here are some other facts that you may be interested to know about water;

When brain cells have a sufficient amount of drinking water they are able to circulate fresh oxygen-laden blood freely through the brain. This allows the brain to remain fresh and alert. Even a small decrease in the amount of water you drink every day can make a difference in your brain's performance. It can actually drop your brain performance as much as twenty to thirty percent.

Water keeps your eyes and mouth moist; it washes dirt and dust away from your eyes and lubricates your mouth which is important when trying to speak. When you are learning to speak again, it is easier to do so with a wet whistle than a dry pasty one.

Our bodies use drinking water to digest food in our stomach. A lack of water will slow the process of digestion which may also lead to constipation or other discomforts.

Your muscles are able to work longer without tiring. As long as you continue to have a good supply of drinking water which continues to supply oxygen to the muscles, you continue to be hydrated which becomes very important especially in hot weather.

Speaking of hot weather, your body temperature is maintained through the use of water. The water regulates your body temperature through sweat when it's hot. Sweat cools the body, but sweat uses up your water supply. This is just another reason to drink plenty of water.

Your nerve cells transmit messages to and from the brain. To do this they use electrolytes. Drinking water is an important way to maintain electrolytes at such a level that your nerves can do their work.

Your kidneys filter waste which leaves your body in the form of urine which is almost entirely water, so you must constantly replace that water to avoid a build up of toxins in the body that may make you sick.

Stay away from the high sugar, high caffeine energy drinks; they will do you more harm than good.

"Resentment is like drinking poison
and then hoping it will kill your enemies".
—Nelson Mandela
Winner of the Nobel Peace Prize

Anger

Anger is the cloud that hides the sun

Anger will slow down or completely stop the rehabilitation process. It is hard enough learning new things with a brain injury; it is even harder when you are angry or upset about something.

Think about a time when you were at work or school and you couldn't focus on your job or project because you were angry at someone from the argument you had last night. You may just nod your head, you're not paying attention, you are just thinking about how to get even with that person. This drains so much energy from you. Energy you could put to good use learning new things. So when someone or something makes you angry or does you wrong you have some choices: you can talk about it and straighten out the situation immediately, you can change the way you think about it or you can simply let it go.

"What, let it go? But I can't let it go!" That is probably the hardest thing to do for most people because there is that feeling of revenge.

I will get even. Getting even is a form of self-pity; it is a virus that will drag you down very fast to a place where no one wants to be. You may think, "They will never say that to me again". Well that may make you feel better for a little while but if you look back at past events in your life there are things you wish you had let go, because now you don't talk to the person involved or you feel very uncomfortable when you are in their company. You avoid them on the street and think to yourself, "If I would have let this go, I wouldn't feel this way right now".

So the next time you run into a difficult situation, stop and think before you react or speak. That simple pause, thinking about how you will react can reduce a lot of stress and anxiety in the future. Your response to the event will determine the outcome, so unless someone backs over your new car with a bull-dozer on purpose try to let things go. If someone really does something bad to you it might be a good idea to part ways and have nothing to do with that person at all. After my accident, I was angry for a few years. Angry at the driver for talking on the cell phone, angry at the fire department for getting me out of the car, angry with myself for now being such a burden on my family and friends. All of this anger created a massive energy drain and really made me tired. When you are tired something as little as a person chewing gum too loud can tick you off!

Remember this; anger is created by YOU and YOU alone, not your family, not your friends, not the doctors that told you that you will be better in a few months and you're angry because it has not happened yet. You control how you react to the things that come your way. I'm not saying keep everything bottled up like a volcano ready to explode at the first thing you see one day. Sometimes it is good to get things off your chest, vent your anger, hurts and frustration, so you can say "That feels better".

Getting angry for a short time is a lot easier than brewing up a long costly plan to get even. It is like trying to pour more water into a glass that is already full, you just make a mess.

You must first empty the glass by expressing your feelings and concerns to make room for more. First let others do the same, listen to them and let them express their hopes and dreams, fears and concerns, hurts and pains, before you talk about yours. It opens up a space inside of them to be able to listen and take in what you have to say. When you channel those energies into helping yourself and others you are on the road to success and your success is the ultimate payback, not revenge.

Four categories that trigger our anger.

1. We become angry when someone demeans or attacks our self-esteem.
2. We become angry when someone or something prevents us from reaching a significant goal that we believe is rightfully ours.
3. We become angry when someone or something violates our basic principles or values, such as fair play or honesty. (someone who cheats when you play golf. I am not going to mention any names ...)
4. We become angry when we feel helpless to correct a "wrong" in our lives or to fix a situation that has gone bad.

Overcoming Anger

Here are some tips for overcoming anger that I have used myself to get out of this dark cloud.

- Getting to know your early warning signs will give you a heads- up for what is to come. I have gotten to know myself inside and out so that I could detect the early warning signs of anger. We all have them - some are different than others but either way they're sending your body a signal. I would start to feel symptoms of a hot face. I could feel it burning, I would clench my teeth together, tighten my fists and I could feel my heart racing. These symptoms then became my signal to step back take a deep breath and think about the situation. For example a driver would cut me off in traffic and give me the middle finger. Something so little would set me off in a rage. The reason was, I took it personally. I didn't know what was going on in that person's life - maybe his wife just left him or his dog just died. I stopped wasting my time trying to figure out why people in this world are mean to each other and all it is, is a waste of time and energy. It is none of my business what others think of me. Treat people the way you want to be treated.

• Reason with yourself, become an expert on yourself, keep an anger diary - the triggers, frequency and intensity. Is there a pattern? Are there particular people or situations? My dad's first wife was killed by a train when her vehicle was hit at a crossing. Growing up I remember him getting angry every time he heard or saw a train. Begin to reason with yourself. Is it worth it? Are you justified?

• Practice thought stopping, think of a word you can say aloud to trigger your brain to interrupt your thought pattern so that you don't allow those negative thoughts into your head. Chad shared with me that his signal is 'lights on, lights off.' In his mind with those simple words he can shut off the negative thoughts just as easy as a light switch and leave those angry thoughts in the dark where they should be.

• Avoid overstimulation. Care for yourself through nutrition, rest and exercise; take care of your physical well-being as well as your mental health.

• Practice effective communication. Don't beat around the bush. Many people become angry because they take things the wrong way. Say what you mean and mean what you say and have a good day. "Hey, that rhymes!"

• Practice empathy; see life through someone else's eyes. Just like the guy who cut me off in traffic, maybe he's also going through a bad time in his life.

• Practice tolerance, accept people as they are not as you would like them to be; have fewer rules about how you expect people around you to behave and live their lives.

• Practice forgiveness, wipe your chalkboard clear so to speak … just let it go.

• Practice relaxation, find a quiet area where you can take some deep breaths and relax.

• Laugh at yourself.

As you can see there are four things that set people off to become angry but there are far more ways not to be angry.

These are just a few.

**"Forrest is doing well, but we need to keep
him for a few more days because
I'm lonely and he's funny."**

Laughter

"Dear funny bone, I miss you dearly. When this cast comes off of my arm, I hope you are still there."

For years I denied myself the one thing that in the end would be one of the keys to unlock me from the shackles of depression and anxiety, and that was laughter. I don't know why I denied myself of it, sometimes when I would laugh I would feel guilty thinking the worst. Maybe the doctors and therapists would think I wasn't taking my recovery seriously. I really don't know why. Maybe because it is not something to laugh at, I don't know. But lucky for me I realized that laughter is the best medicine (unless of course you have a stomach infection, then penicillin works better).

Once you learn to laugh and to laugh at yourself you can truly begin to heal inside and out. It was a couple of years after the accident before I had a good laugh, a very good one, you know the kind when your stomach hurts and your eyes begin to water. Wow!

I thought "I haven't felt like this since I was a kid!" It was euphoria. From then on I thought, "This can't be wrong, it feels so good." So I made sure that I would laugh and smile every day. I watched funny television shows and funny movies, anything that was a comedy and made me feel better. The force that propels human action is emotions and feelings, not cold cognitions. If you love what you're doing it is much easier to do it. And if you could have a laugh at the same time ... even better.

This goes for speech therapy, occupational therapy and all the other therapies out there. If the person has no interest in it or no personal connection to the project there will be no motivation to complete the task. In therapy there must be a way to personalize each project that a person is working on, even in the slightest way. It might just be the spark to ignite that person to get motivated to be well and to help themselves heal.

Laughter increases endorphin levels.

Endorphins are tiny chemicals in the brain that reduce pain and anxiety and increase the feeling of well-being. They also stimulate the immune system. Some of the other events in our life that release endorphins are eating chocolate, sunbathing, exercising and falling in love. All of these things will make a person feel good. If you want someone to fall in love with you feed them chocolate on a treadmill on a sunny day. Take a few minutes out of your day and find something to laugh and smile about.

Here are some facts about laughter and smiling:

• Women smile more than men.

• It takes only seventeen muscles to smile compared to forty-three to frown.

• A smile is a universal expression of happiness and is recognized as such by all cultures so even if you are unable to speak at this point just smile, it will make you feel good as well as others around you.

• A smiling person is judged to be more pleasant, attractive, sincere, sociable and competent.

• Happy people generally don't get sick as

often as people who are unhappy. There is an old saying "people in love don't catch colds"

• People are born with the ability to smile. Even babies, who are born blind, smile.

• Generally, adults laugh approximately fifteen times per day, while children laugh around four hundred times a day.

• People who smile often live longer.

• Laughter needs no translation

Try this little test today.

Smile at everyone you see, and laugh often. At the end of the day, notice how you feel and whether people acted differently around you.

It took some practice for me to do this, but what I did was stand in front of a mirror every morning for about ten minutes with a huge grin on my face. The smile led to laughter so as I went about my day I couldn't stop giggling every time I thought of myself standing in front of the mirror. Try it for yourself. I know it sounds goofy but it works.

Happiness leads to smiling and smiling leads to happiness. Happiness is your natural immunity, having a great positive effect on your health and well-being. If you don't feel like smiling, smile anyway. It's a start.

Take this ninety day free trial of smiling and laughing and then decide if you want to return to the old miserable you or if you enjoy being happy. Then keep it up for the rest of your life and share it with everyone.

"I will never understand all the good
that a simple smile can accomplish"
—Mother Teresa.

Marriage

In marriage it is important to treat all of your disasters as incidents and none of your incidents as disasters.

One thing that has to be said up front about marriage to the person with acquired brain injury, that is not warm and fuzzy is this, do not be angry with your wife or husband for what has happened to you, they did not do this, it is not their fault for what is going on in your life. Realize that if they are there with you they obviously love you. So don't push them away and they will then give you the same in return.

If you feel that you're getting angry and into a fighting mood lay down on the couch for a few minutes. I find it is very difficult to be angry when I'm lying down. It may sound silly but try it. You may also find it helpful to go back to the anger section of this book and review a few strategies for overcoming anger.

One thing you can do if you are the spouse of a survivor and tensions are heating up is to take a time out. My wife used to do this with me. When an argument started she would say "give me a minute to think about this". What this did was cause a delay and it gave time to clear the air and defuse the situation and most of the time I didn't even realize it had happened. If you can't speak, use the 'T' symbol with your hands like a referee does at a football game meaning 'time out'.

The other option you have is to keep yelling at your partner and the next thing you know you'll find yourself alone and the only one you will have to yell at is yourself in a very lonely house. Please keep this in mind. I have seen it happen to too many people and it would be nice to prevent others from doing the same just by reading and taking in this section of the book. I can't say it any clearer: treat your spouse with disrespect and you'll find yourself alone without a spouse.

Statistics say that only one in twenty couples will stay married after one of the partners receives a brain injury. Wow! That is only five percent. A lot of people I have met with brain injuries will say "My partner is not the same person I married". Well, perhaps that's true. But with your help and support possibly they will be a better person than before. Remember "For better or worse."

I understand how frustrating it must be for a husband or wife living with someone with a brain injury and it is compounded even more when you add children into the picture. If you truly care for that person try to stick it out through the good times and the bad. It takes time to recover from this, lots of time, and it is also the time that that person needs you the most. You wouldn't plant a seed in the ground and come back the next day looking at the ground and feeling rejected that the plant hasn't sprouted yet. So don't expect your partner to be the same as before the injury just after a few months of rehabilitation. Plant the seed, have patience; nurture it and you will watch your relationship grow into something wonderful.

Remember, it is okay to say "I don't know", or "Please help me with this." Being humble goes a long way. Recognize the fact that your partner has the right to be different, and that they are not you. Finally, remember your partner is not the clay and you are not the potter so don't try to mold them into what you want. Let me ask you this, have you ever wanted someone to change? And did they because you wanted them to?

Practice a little "live and let live". Most people I have met dislike being told "You're wrong". You have a right to your own opinion but sometimes it is better to keep it to yourself.

Sure there are times when I thought of packing it in, and just saying "To hell with this. I don't need this crap. I'm out of here." But they were only thoughts. Once I cooled down I would think things over and realize things would not be better somewhere else. I knew that my problems would just come with me wherever I went, so it was up to me to change my thoughts and my attitude. My marriage is now fifteen years young. Over half of that time, nine years, I have been living with a brain injury and so have my wife and son. So as time goes by, things do get better. In the beginning it is a rough and rocky road and yes it does suck!

But know this, if you work at it everything improves slowly but surely. Small changes over time become a massive change.

Remember, if you are not loved, nothing else matters, not the car you drive, the house you live in, 'nothing'.

In volunteering at a retirement home I have met many interesting people. One couple that I have got to know very well over the last few years is Max and Eva. They have been married for sixty-seven years, so I thought if I want advice on how to keep a marriage together for many years these would be the people to ask. So I interviewed them for this book. I simply asked them what the secret to a long marriage was. They said there was no secret. It was in fact very simple. Here are a few of the points they made to me.

• Never go to bed angry at each other just in case you never wake up, you sleep better.

• They walk together every day. Fresh air is the key even if it is ten minutes after supper in a snow storm. Make time! You don't even have to talk to each other on the walk, just enjoy the scenery and time together.

• They say to watch your pennies and to spend less than you make. Most marriage failures that they have seen over the years ended because of financial problems. They say to talk about your finances together and only make large purchases together .

• Let things go. Ask yourself before you get angry; "Is this really important?" Forgive.

• Have a sense of humour. Most of life's troubles don't seem so big if you can both have a laugh about it.

• Rest every day even if it is for ten or fifteen minutes. It will recharge your batteries and leave you with a better outlook on things.

• Never let your marriage turn into a two-headed coin ... that's when you're stuck together but you can't face each other. Try to work things out.

"*Every morning you are handed 24 golden hours. They are one of few things in this world that you get free of charge.*
If you had all the money in the world, you could not buy an extra hour. What will you do with this priceless treasure? Remember, you must use it, as it is given only once. Once wasted it is never given back."
—*James Thomson, Brain Injury Survivor*

What?

Problems with attention

"Hey, the bird feeder is empty!"

Looking back now, my wife can tell me what an average day was like after I came home from the hospital. I would have to constantly be reminded to stay focused on what I was doing. My friends gave me the nick-name "Ping", because I was like a ping-pong ball bouncing back and forth, back and forth. I was all over the place but not getting anything done.

One day I was brushing my teeth and I looked out the window and thought "Hey, the bird feeder is empty", so I put my toothbrush down and went outside to fill the bird feeder. Only later did I realize that I had not finished brushing my teeth, shaving or combing my hair. To the outside world it would look like I was lazy or I didn't care about myself anymore but really it was neither. Had I forgotten to do the simple things in the morning? Or was I just distracted?

I think now I was just easily distracted by many things like background noise or change of scenery. This went on for a few years until I was able to focus clearly on each task I was doing. This area takes a lot of work because you are easily distracted. It is hard to focus on any one thing for a period of time. When you do learn to focus, you can do anything in the world.

Your mind works the same way as a magnifying glass, with the sun behind you focus the magnifying glass on a piece of paper. If done for a long enough time it will catch fire every time but if you move the magnifying glass around nothing happens - you're just wasting your time.

Some things around the house that you could do to prevent any accidents would be to first focus on one thing at a time such as:

Cooking.

If you are cooking, stay in the kitchen and watch the stove until your meal is complete. The old saying goes "A watched pot never boils". Believe me it does, even more if you don't watch it. If you go into the other room to watch the television you could start a fire.

I know, I've done this.

Children

You should not leave a child in the bathtub to go answer the phone because it is very dangerous. I had also left my son home alone when I left the house and forgot he was there sleeping and let me tell you this caused a lot of friction with the whole family.

Tools

If you are working with tools be aware of your surroundings and focus on what you are doing or you could injure yourself. I know this too, I've done it many times. Believe me it is not a good thing when the emergency room staff knows you by your first name.

These statements may seem very basic and may be obvious to most people. But to the person with a brain injury, sometimes all it takes is a phone to ring or the doorbell to go off and you lose concentration immediately from what you are doing.

When you slow down and focus on what you are doing you will get more done. You must complete each task to the end and make this a habit; once this becomes a routine the speed will follow.

Just like the magnifying glass: if you move around from task to task nothing gets accomplished, no job will be complete and you will become overwhelmed with the back-log in your life. So once again, you have to focus.

I know what it is like to want to prove to everyone and to yourself that you're just as good as you used to be at this point. Well, you may not be. So take a step back and know your limitations. If you re-learn your skills safely you may be able to do the things you used to, but if you go out and hurt yourself or someone else this will create doubt in yourself and others about your abilities and it will slow down your recovery process.

"Happiness does not depend on outward things, but on the way we see them."
—Leo Tolstoy, Novelist and philosopher

The Christmas Party Theory

For friends and family to understand how difficult it is for a person with an Acquired Brain Injury to pay attention in everyday situations I try to explain it like your work Christmas party.

You are at the company party engaged in a conversation when suddenly you hear your name mentioned in a nearby conversation. You turn your attention to the conversation next to you where you heard your name and suddenly you find that you can no longer hear the conversation you were originally involved in.

This occurs because your brain cannot process two conversations at a time. With an Acquired Brain Injury it may not be another conversation in the room but a radio or television that is the distraction, so when possible pay attention to your surroundings and background noise. It will be much easier to get your message across.

So many times I would nod my head as if I understood what you were saying but I did not, simply because I was distracted by something.

"If you put small value on yourself, rest assured that the world will not raise your price."—Anonymous

The Power of Three

I remember the first time I saw my now close friend Chad. I was at a brain injury conference in Barrie, Ontario held by the March of Dimes. I was mesmerized by that infectious smile of his. I immediately liked him and I didn't even know his name yet.

I wanted to have his outlook and I thought to myself how can someone who has gone through a life changing brain injury be so happy and positive? His secret was helping others. He told me of his volunteering and coaching of kids. If it worked for him, could it possibly work for me? Well, fast forward five years and yes, it does work and I love it. I volunteer at a retirement home in my own town and I now make it a habit to do three nice things a day: one for myself, one for my family and one for a stranger. I call it the power of three. The power of three has brought so much into my life. I really want for nothing other than to give more.

It works the same way as the most powerful tool in the world, 'Compound interest'. The way compound interest works is this: you put a little money away every week or month in your account and don't touch it. For a few years you probably won't see much of a change while it just putts along growing very slowly and then eventually you'll see explosive growth; your money will double and if you leave it long enough it will double again and so on. That little amount that you put in at the beginning has now turned into super numbers. Well, if you did a minimum of three nice things a day you will be rewarded with compound interest in the form of joy, love, confidence, opportunities, success and many other things just by knowing that you helped so many people in their lives. There are many others that would love the chance to give back to you in any way they can.

When you do something nice for someone it is not just them who would love to give back to you it is also their family and their friends. This is where the fifty dollars a week turns into one million by virtue of compound interest. Just imagine if you did three nice things a day for one year - that is over one thousand good things you have done. Now, can you imagine if one thousand good things happened to you over a period of one year how different your life would be?

I know that it has made massive changes in my life. So take some interest in people and invest some time and before you know it you'll be rich in many ways. Doing these nice things can be as simple as holding doors open, putting your dishes away, looking a stranger in the eye, or talking to someone who's in a wheelchair. Smile and say hello. This is a big one for me as I was in a wheelchair for a few months. I also have many good friends in wheelchairs and I wouldn't trade that time for all the money in the world, because I learned so much about myself and society. For some reason people don't make a lot of eye contact with you when you are confined to a chair. I would like to change that by sharing with as many people as I can that a person in a chair is no different than you or I, and that everyone has a sense of humour and feelings. We are all human - there is no difference - so the next time you meet a person in a wheelchair treat them with the same respect as the person standing beside you. Please.

Help a neighbour cut grass or shovel snow. Help someone learn to read or write. There are a million of nice things to do and millions of rewards for doing them. The first and greatest reward is feeling good about you. It is a great confidence builder for both you and the person you help. Chad and I have become good friends and we both continue to do what we can to help others.

"Confidence is contagious;
so is the lack of it."
—*Anonymous*

The Face of an Angel

"I kissed the face of an angel, but I didn't get to say goodbye"

Volunteering is a big part in the recovery process. Dr. Coutts had said it would help get me back around people and really help with my social skills. At first I tried volunteering at my son's school doing lunch duty and monitoring and I was also the hotdog guy on hotdog days. I have to admit that didn't last long. I couldn't handle 300 kids running and screaming, it was just too overwhelming. I thought of volunteering at the hospital to give back to the people who helped me. My doctor suggested it may be too soon because of the depression I was going through. It would be harder to see more people going through the same thing at this time, so my occupational therapist Claudia Maurice said she had a friend, Janice Arbour, who ran the recreation activities at a local retirement lodge so off I went.

I have to admit my first day there was very intimidating. I didn't know what to expect, but to my surprise it was not at all what I expected. I was introduced as the new volunteer for recreation activities such as cards and shuffleboard. The first woman I met there was Margaret. She was an angel. She came up and gave me a big hug and said "welcome aboard!" Margaret was full of vim, vigor and vitality. She was fun -loving and carefree and always had a big hug and kiss for me and my son who I brought with me every week. She always had funny sayings like "Family is like fudge, sweet with a few nuts." The nice thing about Margaret and all the other people there was that they didn't care what I drove, how I dressed, whether I had forgotten to comb my hair or if I stuttered. As it turns out they wanted the same thing as me: love, attention and companionship. That wasn't very hard to give and believe me it wasn't hard to get back in return. Margaret and my son Hunter had a little secret. She would sneak him into the kitchen and fill him with cookies. She was a real sweetheart.

The week after Christmas Hunter and I returned for shuffleboard as always on Tuesday night. We were knocking on doors up and down the halls to round up all the regular players when we noticed Margaret's room was empty. She had passed away just after Christmas. That was a real heartbreaker for both of us and it was then that I realized I had kissed the face of an angel, but I didn't get to say goodbye.

Everybody in the world is so busy with their lives and we forget that life will one day end. And we don't know when that day will be. So please tell all of the people you love and care for, how much you love them, how important they are to you, before it's too late. I hope you find a Margaret in your life. I hope you find an angel.

People who know me know that I love to give hugs to everyone. That is important in my life. It not only makes me feel good but I believe it makes the people themselves feel good and I believe that a hug from someone can do more for you in life than any pill or medical device out there. A hug can raise your spirits when you're feeling low and skyrocket them when you're feeling good. Go ahead and try it for a week and I bet that you keep on doing it for life.

One thing Margaret said that stuck in my head was, "Relax and take a turtle for a walk." At first I did not understand what she was talking about but I do now. It may seem silly but I did take a turtle for a walk. By that I mean I walked down my road very, very slowly just like a turtle and I noticed so many things that I hadn't noticed before like the bees on a flower, the sound of the wind blowing through the leaves and all the other things we take for granted as we rush along in our busy lives. I hope you can find it in yourself to take a turtle for a walk. You will discover all of these different little things that are very calming and you will also see many of your worries going away, at least for a little while.

"Example is not the main thing influencing others. It is the only thing."
—Albert Schweitzer, Medical missionary

Get Rid of the BMW's

Bitchers, Moaners and Whiners

Have you ever made progress in your recovery listening to others bitch about how bad they have it? No? So why do it? If you are the person bitching and moaning please stop now. You're only digging yourself into a hole and no one wants to be with you. If you ever find yourself in that hole, stop digging!

If you don't believe me, look around you. Are there less people phoning you? Has the number of people coming to visit you decreased? These may well be signals that you are turning into a negative person that no one wants to be around. And the signals are everywhere. You just have to open your eyes to see them.

Perhaps your girlfriend or boyfriend keeps cancelling their date with you or the guys from work don't ask you to join them for a get together on the weekend. Believe me, it's not because you have a brain injury. So you can give up the victim mentality, it's because of the way you are acting. Sometimes people think that if they act out in anger they will get more attention. This may be true but is this the type of attention you want?

I was recently in my physiotherapist's office and a mother pushed her teenage boy in a wheelchair into the room, It was clear he had a broken leg and looked uncomfortable and while we were in the waiting room all he did was bitch at his mother. "How come it takes so long? This place sucks, I'm tired of this crap, and I shouldn't have to wait." I felt so bad for the mother. You could tell she was so embarrassed. This young man needed a lesson in manners; he also needed to realize that his mother was his caregiver. The word is very self-explanatory.

"Caregiver". That's what they do, they care for you. And you want to treat them like a piece of garbage? It is no wonder why so many families break up and people get divorced after something tragic happens to a family member.

So my advice to the person with a brain injury would be to think before you speak and ask yourself, "Is this really important?" Every one has to wait in line. You too. So just take a deep breath and relax; the person that brought you there did so because they love you. So why would you want to act out in a manner that would drive that person away from you?

The next time you're in a situation like that and you want to speak up and be heard by everyone in the waiting room or pharmacy or wherever it is you are, tell them some good news. That is guaranteed to get people's attention. Good news does more than get attention; good news pleases people and helps them relax. You could say things like, "This is my fourteenth time in physiotherapy and I feel much better than I did when I first came. This place is great and the people make you feel welcome!"

That is something positive that will create interest from others in the waiting room - then you may have the opportunity to explain your situation or your injury in a positive manner. Telling them how far you've come will be an inspiration to everyone there rather than telling them how bad things are and that you can't use your leg anymore until you get the cast off.

Now you might be able to see how you can get the same point across and be positive and attract people to you instead of having people push away from you. Remember to respect and love your caregivers who are always there for you. I realize that when you are angry the easiest ones to hurt are the ones that love you and are closest to you.

I don't know why that is.

I've done it many times myself and now wish I could take it all back after seeing how many people who have been hurt by my anger. So I hope the pages in this book will allow you to avoid a lot of the pain and anguish that I went through and that I put my family through. Once again, before you burst out with your bitching and whining because little Jimmy spilled juice on the table just ask yourself, "Is this really important"? When you ask that question it gives you a moment to think rather than reacting immediately. It has helped me in many situations so possibly write that point down and stick it on your fridge until it becomes a habit.

Caregiver Overload

Don't fall into the trap of
"Caregiver overload."

At the time of writing this I have been visiting two close friends in the hospital, neither one with a brain injury. But as time passes I can see the toll it takes on the person being a caregiver and wanting to be there every moment. I have spent quite a bit of time with each of the caregivers of these friends explaining the dangers of making themselves sick both physically and emotionally if they don't take care of themselves. And if this happens they won't be able to take care of their loved one when they need them the most.

Caring for a person with acquired brain injury requires quite a bit of your time and energy. Yes, it can be a very rewarding experience. But it can also be demanding and stressful taking a lot out of you physically and emotionally. If you see any of the following ten signs of stress over-whelming yourself or someone you care about please take action and get some help.

- Denial about the injury and the future effects it will have on the person with the injury. "Don't worry; Forrest is going to be fine, there is nothing wrong. Everyone is just over-reacting right now. Just give him some time."

- Anxiety about what the future holds. For both you and the injured one. "I don't know what I'm going to do when the nurses are gone, I don't know if I can take care of him on my own."

- Anger at the person with a brain injury. "If he says I don't remember one more time I'm going to lose it, I'm going to snap." Or "That is the fourth time today she has asked me that question, I can't take this anymore."

- Becoming a turtle. Hiding in your shell will not make the world go away, nor will it make things any better. You may no longer want to stay in touch with your friends or do social activities that you did all the time. You may even say "I just don't care about anything anymore."

- Depression or hopelessness is common feelings at this time but if not looked after, you could be the one needing care. You may have feelings like you don't care anymore or feel what's the use? Why should I keep trying? Depression will drag you down faster than anything; try not to fall into the trap of it. You do have a choice.

• Exhaustion, where you don't have the energy to do anything. Completing daily tasks and chores becomes an overwhelming experience because of your fatigue.

• Lack of sleep can cause many problems. You may wake up many times in the middle of the night, have bad dreams or nightmares about the situation ... where your mind cannot stop racing and it feels like a television on which someone keeps changing the channel on you. Lack of sleep can be a cause of so many problems.

• Emotional overload. I often say that people with acquired brain injury wear their emotions on their sleeves but I now see that caregivers do also. You may cry when you hear a sad song or for no reason at all, you're often irritable. Simple little things that you would dismiss before such as running out of dog food, now become a big emotional event. "You knew the dog food was low, why the hell didn't you pick up more?"

• Memory problems and lack of concentration

sometimes go hand in hand and you will blame your lack of concentration on your bad memory. You may have trouble completing tasks that once seemed simple, or completing a regular task that you once did daily. "I used to read the newspaper daily, now I can't even focus on one story".

• Deteriorating health. You may be so focused on the person you're caring for, that you're denying yourself good health care, diet and exercise. You may find yourself losing or gaining weight. You also may develop other problems such as chronic headaches, back pain or high blood pressure and stress.

"All of life is a chance. So take it!
The person who goes furthest is the one
who is willing to do and dare."
—Dale Carnegie, Author and Trainer

Me First

Reduce caregiver stress and overload

As a caregiver you need to take care of yourself in order to take care of your loved one. Just think of what would happen to your loved one if you are gone or become bedridden yourself. If you have ever flown on an airplane you will know that the first safety tip they show you if the cabin becomes depressurized is to put your oxygen mask on first before you help others. This makes perfect sense because you can't help others with their breathing if you cannot breathe yourself.

"Take care of yourself first."

I really believe that the caregivers are the forgotten ones. Many people think only about the injured person but in my eyes I believe they should be thinking about the caregivers and ways they can help them to reduce stress. The caregiver is probably the most important person in a recovering person's life and not only do they have to take care of the recovering person but everything else falls on their shoulders. They have to take care of themselves and their children, the bills, the home and car maintenance, making meals and cleaning ... the list goes on and on. These people should have a national holiday named after them because they are super people. The bad thing I see is that caregivers have to put up with a lot of crap in many cases. I know my wife did in my case, and for a long time I wondered why she stayed with me. I would have left me for the way I was acting. So on behalf of all people living with a brain injury I would like to thank all the caregivers and apologize to all of you who may have been hurt. My hope is that you can reduce a lot of your stress by reading these next few tips. Just try a few and I'm sure they'll work because you deserve to have a lot less stress in your life for everything you do.

Ten ways to reduce caregiver stress and overload.

• Learn as much as you can about brain injury. As my friend Carol says, "Knowledge is power." There are many books and websites you can use for information. The more you understand the effects of brain injury the easier it will be to identify with your loved one and what they may be going through. But you may also reduce your stress knowing that some of these things are common that you are going through. You are not unique in your anguish and its effects.

• Give healing its time and be realistic about the healing process and the amount of time it takes. Every injury is different. No two are the same so there is no straight answer as to when your loved one will recover. But know that it does take time, patience and love. It doesn't happen overnight, it happens over time.

• Get to know yourself and what you are capable of doing. You can't do everything on your own. So get your priorities in order whatever they may be and write them down. For a while you may have to give up something you love to do in order to make time for your loved one.

• Have a good belly laugh! Laugher is a natural stress reliever that helps to lower blood pressure, slows your heart rate and breathing rate and relaxes your muscles. There is nothing funny about brain injury but it is important to make an effort to look on the lighter side of life. It is impossible to be sad or angry while you're laughing; if you don't believe me just try it.

It is important to have a good laugh with the brain injured person because laughter releases endorphins into the brain which causes a sense of well-being and also reduces levels of pain and anxiety.

If the caregiver and survivor can find a way to laugh together many of those big problems won't seem so big anymore. Go out and get a funny movie tonight.

• Watch your diet and choose foods carefully. You may not realize it but the food you are eating may be causing some of your stress. Inadequate nutrition increases stress on your body. Fatty foods full of sugar as well as processed foods seem to increase stress in most people. Lean meat, chicken, whole grains, fresh fruits and vegetables seem to decrease stress. You may think "Let's order a pizza; I'm too stressed to cook." Give it a second thought. Is it a good idea?

• Exercise can reduce stress greatly. Even if you take a ten or fifteen minute walk around the hospital or down the street it will reduce your stress levels immensely, you will also find that you think a little clearer after a walk.

• Become a better breather. While visiting in Toronto General Hospital recently I couldn't help but notice signs everywhere: "Breath deeply." I asked a nurse, "What's up with the signs?" She said "Stress can cause shallow breathing" which means that your body won't get enough oxygen to fully relax. Learn to breathe more slowly and deeply from your abdomen. One way to do this is to imagine that you have a small beach ball behind your belly button, which you slowly inflate and deflate. Practice that for a while and you'll notice a great reduction in stress.

• Squish the ANTS (automatic negative thoughts). Most of our anxiety is self-induced, meaning that we reap what we sow. If you're often thinking that the worst case scenarios are going to happen they usually do. Start thinking about the good things in life and how well things are going to be in the future and you will see that good things do come your way. Think positive. Read positive books or listen to some good music that will cheer you up. Squish those damn ANTS!

• Get used to your feelings being on that roller coaster ride of up and down. Accept that you will have feelings of being happy, angry, guilty, embarrassed and sad and know that there is no right or wrong way to feel at this time. Let your feelings out, it's okay to cry. You may want to pound on the pillow or go outside and scream in the car. Whatever it is don't be shy. Let your feelings out, don't bottle them up.

• Join a support group. There are many people out there going through the same thing you are. You are not alone. Ask your nurse or health care provider for a list of support groups in your area. It can really help to reduce your stress if you can talk to someone going through the same thing as you are. Chances are you will also receive many helpful tips that can help in so many ways on your journey through recovery. It is also nice to know you have the support behind you of people who have been through the same thing and are willing to share their thoughts and feelings with you, and who are also there to listen to yours.

"Nothing stops the man who desires to achieve.
Every obstacle is simply a course to develop his
achievement muscle. It's strengthening of his
powers of accomplishment."
—Thomas Carlyle, Author

A Case for Organization

I first met Mary Lee LaPosta of Stratus Home Solutions.ca a few years ago when she did a presentation for the March of Dimes on the advantages of organization while living with an acquired brain injury. I asked Mary Lee to write something for this book because I have seen firsthand what a difference it can make in a life just by getting organized. Here are some tips written by Mary Lee. I hope you can take something from them and apply them in your life to make things easier.

Are you aware that physical and/or emotional clutter can leave a "cloud" hanging over your head...and your life? A person with an acquired brain injury will usually have a larger "cloud" than those without an injury. Life can be overwhelming in the best of circumstances but tackling daily chores and dealing with schedules will definitely be much more difficult for those with an acquired brain injury.

Studies have shown that a patient's adjustment can be deeply impacted by mild impairments in functions such as short-term memory. The extra effort, vigilance, and concentration needed to compensate for such mild deficits result in an enormous fatiguing effect. Such an effort produces a continuous drain on energy levels and results in chronic fatigue. Intellectual functions such as short-term memory tend to deteriorate as fatigue increases. Such practices give rise to a vicious cycle that leads to feelings of inadequacy, discouragement, irritability and depression.

Some common results of brain injury are difficulties with memory, mood and concentration. Others include significant deficits in organizational and reasoning skills, learning, cognitive, and executive functions. There is a great need for certain adjustments and accommodations during the recovery period (which could last a lifetime in some cases). The need for assessing, implementing and maintaining an organizational plan is a crucial step for those living with an acquired brain injury.

Most individuals with acquired brain injuries who are living in their own homes will have the assistance of several support staff and workers as well as family members and friends who will visit whether on a daily or weekly basis. Unfortunately, not all of these support staff and/or workers will have the exact same idea as to where to find items in your home or where to put them. It is primarily up to you to decide where items should be kept or stored. Your unique needs should always be the priority of anyone who enters the home.

You might be performing certain housekeeping chores (meals, cleaning etc) on your own as well as with the assistance of others. In order to make sure everyone is on the "same page" it is essential that everyone is made aware of your individual needs whether it be where items in the kitchen are to be stored or where to find or store other items in and around your home. It can become quite stressful if all involved are not on the same page. Sometimes, an organizer (someone who has experience and/or knowledge of organizing) may need to be hired. This is someone who can assess your unique needs and can also address the concerns and needs of anyone involved with you in your home.

The process can be as simple as reorganizing the kitchen cupboards and placing labels or instructions throughout the home or as complex as de-cluttering/organizing the entire home as well as creating, implementing and displaying daily structured plan sheets, setting up your Personal Device or Smartphone for scheduled "reminders" or "appointments", moving furniture to assist in your mobility needs and posting colour coded information or reminders throughout the home.

To be most efficient and have the best outcomes for Acquired Brain Injured patients, a collaborative approach among all those working to help support the patient is desirable. Protocols such as information sharing (a general communication binder) as well as identifying areas of responsibility for all involved should be assessed and implemented.

It is essential to encourage increased independence from the start by implementing an organizational plan for the patient as well as anyone else who is involved in their care. The type and level of support is as unique as the person and their experience.

The goals of an organizer normally include:

- Maximizing the patient's mobility (assessing furniture placement) and activities of daily living including communication Implementing plans to improve attention span, memory, judgement and physical function
- Educating the patient, their family and support staff of their individualized needs
- Reducing stimulation in the environment such as activity and noise levels
- Providing routines for patients

A formalized organizational plan should be monitored daily and requires a consistent team and family effort. An organizer can help those with cognitive and personal challenges improve their efficiency and quality of life through personal organizing techniques and strategies and to provide real life answers to problems which many Acquired Brain Injury patients face during their day to day activities.

Here are some of the key benefits that organization can bring to your life as you recover from your brain injury:

• Reduce Stress! Clutter is a main contributing factor of household stress. An organizer can reduce your stress tremendously by offering many suggestions to reduce emotional and physical clutter which in turn will help all members/occupants/visitors of the home.

• Save Time! Reduce the time spent looking for documents or personal items. An organizer can create and implement unique storage solutions for documents and personal items.

• Save Money! Avoid purchasing duplicate items because you can't find them (or forgot you already bought one). Avoid paying bank and interest charges for not paying bills on time. An organizer can implement many different ways for you to keep track of your monthly bill payments.

• Create More Space (better mobility)! By removing unused and unwanted items you will create fewer barriers while manoeuvring around your home. An organizer can suggest placement of furniture or items in your home so that occupants and visitors can enjoy moving around without the risk of bumps/falls and accidents.

• Enjoy Your Home! Relax or pursue family activities with easy access to books or magazines you really want to read or playing games with your family instead of searching for the missing pieces. An organizer can suggest or implement storage solutions for books/magazines/games etc which will enable you to access them quickly and conveniently.

• Warranty and receipt storage! An organizer will suggest or implement solutions to keep all the small and large appliance warranties and instruction manuals in one place to ensure you do not pay for service calls that may still be covered by the manufacturer.

• Pursue Your Hobby! Finish that project you were working on by having everything you need in one handy spot. An organizer can determine how and where to store your craft or other hobby materials in order that you have full enjoyment of them.

• Reduce Home Hazards! An organizer will remove old paint, chemicals and solvents from the home and bring them to a Household Hazardous Waste recycling depot for you.

• Safety First! An organizer can make sure your first aid kit is up to date and easily accessible, make sure all your emergency exits are un-obstructed, smoke detectors and fire extinguishers are in working order.

Keeping yourself organized and creating "simplicity" is essential.

"Wisdom is the reward you get for a lifetime of listening when you'd have preferred to talk"
—Doug Larson, Author

Therapy

Here are some different types of therapy that may help you in your recovery

Speech and Communication

I would have to say that speech and communication difficulties could be the most frustrating in all of your recovery, because if people do not understand what you are saying or trying to say it will make everyone's life very difficult. It is very frustrating trying to get the message across without a brain injury, and with one the frustration is compounded.

With that said I also believe that speech and communication therapy is also the most rewarding one. Once you have reached your goals, the feeling is so great when you can express what you are thinking and what you want to say comes out clear.

Many of the people that I have met over the years have very similar speech and communication difficulties; the following are just a few of the most common difficulties and examples.

I have trouble finding words

You know what you want to say but the words just won't come out. For example you want to say, "I put it in the stove" and what comes out of your mouth is "the one thing, they are there that that thing!" as you are pointing to the stove like a small child frustrated with not finding the word. But you do know what it is and for some reason that word sticks to the tip of your tongue but will not come out and the harder you try the more frustrated you become.

• Tips for survivors: slow down, you know what you want to say, think for a minute and ask yourself, "what does this thing do"? For example you could say, "that thing you cook on" or "that thing that heats food." When the front door is locked climb the side window to find the word you're looking for or find another way to describe it, and the word will come to you.

• Tips for the caregiver: don't finish the patient's words or sentences, but do help them find the words by asking questions and creating thoughts. This way you can cue them to find the right word. For example you would ask the person "What thing? Over there? What does it do? Does it heat your food?" This way you'll know exactly what the person is talking about. The stove and not the fridge. I found cueing is a very helpful strategy in word finding.

What the @#%$ did he just say?

Oftentimes people with a brain injury will say things that are inappropriate for which I often found myself apologizing. Things would come out of my mouth that you would never hear me say in a million years before the injury. We are all human and we all have thoughts many of which we would ordinarily keep to ourselves. The only way I can describe it is that your brain is like a coffee filter and with a brain injury that coffee filter is torn and sometimes it allows the grinds to get out.

For example you take your wife out to a restaurant and you see the waitress go by and you think, "nice butt" and that thought stays in your mind. But with a brain injury that thought goes right from your brain to your tongue and you blurt out, "nice butt" right in the restaurant and embarrass yourself and your wife. (I am not being sexist here. I have met many women with brain injuries who have done the exact same thing. It's not just men.)

• **Tips for the survivor:** before anything comes out of your mouth make sure that is what you want to say. In the beginning this is very difficult because your coffee filter is torn and only you have the power to fix it. The way you can repair this torn filter takes time and practice so before you speak count to five or ten and make sure that's what you want to say. If you can practice this a little every day you can keep the thoughts in your head that should stay in your head.

• **Tips for the caregiver:** expect this to happen; if you are aware that at some point this is going to happen you will not fly off the handle when it does occur and you can deal with it in a calm and respectful manner. Let them know they should keep those thoughts to themselves and perhaps think next time before they speak. Don't kid yourself by thinking it won't happen. "My wife would never say that she is respectable woman." Like I said earlier, we are all human.

I can't cope with noisy environments

With a brain injury it may be difficult to follow a conversation in a noisy environment such as a shopping mall or restaurant. I found it very difficult being in a large crowd when many people were having several different conversations. This problem can be overcome by working on a few good strategies right in your own home. You can start by having a conversation with a person in your family with all the background noises turned off such as radio and TV and just talk back and forth, then at the end of your conversation go over what you have talked about so you can make sure you are clear about what was said and that there was no misunderstanding. I found it very helpful to do this every day and little by little I was getting better. Eventually when you realize your concentration is getting better you can introduce some background noise such as turning the radio on low and practicing again and again to make sure what is being said is also being understood. That should help prepare you for following a conversation in a noisy environment.

"Find the good. It's all around you. Find it, showcase it and you'll start believing it."
—Jesse Owens, Olympic Gold Medal Athlete

CNN Therapy

This is one that I'm very proud of, not because it works so well for me, but because I discovered it with my speech therapist one day during one of our sessions. You see when people get hungry enough they will eat almost anything; I was hungry for knowledge, wanting to know how I can get better faster.

My speech therapist is awesome but because of economics I was only seeing her three days a week for about an hour a day and it was very helpful. She showed me so many strategies to overcome the difficulties I was struggling with. I had a craving to be better so I had to think of another way that I could practice my speech and reading while Christine was gone.

It turns out it was right in front of me on the TV. You've got it! CNN. Who would've thought that I could overcome so many difficulties watching Anderson Cooper reporting all over the world? CNN had everything I needed to improve my speech, reading, memory and confidence and best of all it was free and available to me 24 hours a day.

Let me explain how it worked for me. But don't get me wrong. You still will get the best benefit from working with a speech language therapist but if you live somewhere where there is not one available or you don't have the funding to pay for one here are some things you can do.

This is not a plug for CNN. There are many channels out there and if you love sports ESPN has the same type of format. The same goes for business CNBC; find what interests you have and it will be much easier.

As you watch CNN you will notice a ticker-tape sliding across the bottom of the screen. What I would do is try to read each word as they pass by. In the beginning it was difficult to get one or two in a row but that didn't matter because I was all alone with all the time in the world. No one was there judging me or rushing me. In the beginning I would also turn the volume off. That was very helpful ... the words will repeat again and again helping you with your memory. It seems very slow in the beginning.

I would say a few words like "the-Bush-war-Desert". After a few months I was able to read full sentences such as "the Bush administration declares war against drugs". I was also able to remember them because it was repeated again and again all day long. It was also a boost to my confidence, because now I was able to start a conversation about current events and because I read and reread these stories they stuck in my memory bank.

As my confidence grew I then proceeded to the next step which was turning up the volume on the TV. What that did was simulate an environment where I was surrounded by people trying to read the ticker-tape while someone was talking. It was very frustrating in the beginning but in the end it was very helpful; it helped me focus on what I was doing and not the background noise.

Eventually I was able to read at the speed the words were passing by and that is a very natural rate of speech. One thing I would have to say to survivors is that you will have to participate in these activities and work at them every day.

You're not going to improve just sitting around waiting for people to show up and help you,

you have to take the initiative to help yourself. It does not matter what type of therapy it is or the obstacle you are trying to overcome. If you persist and truly work at it you will find a way and it may not be the way someone shows you, sometimes you will find your own way. As long as you are trying, you are moving towards long term improvement.

"One way to keep momentum going is to have constantly greater goals."
—Michael Korda, Publisher

Occupational Therapy

This is a very important therapy to get you back on your feet. In the beginning I had no idea what it was about. My first therapist was Gary Warman, a nice guy who spoke very calmly to me. When he came to my house for the first time he had with him a jar with quarters, nickels and dimes. He poured the jar out onto my table and asked me to count a dollar-thirty-five. At that time that was the price of a cup of coffee. I was annoyed. How dare he come into my house and insult my intelligence?

Well as it turns out I could not count money to pay for things in stores so Gary showed me some strategies to help me overcome some of my difficulties. But after the first day I told my wife I did not want to see him again. I felt very ashamed of my shortcomings. The next day Gary returned for another session and after he left my wife said, "I thought you didn't want to see him again?" I replied very sheepishly, "Well yesterday he found some things in me I didn't think I could do, I just want to see if he can find some more". And man did he ever!

I was amazed at the things I was capable of doing when someone put some faith in me and gave me some guidance.

Gary was also somehow able to ease the pain over time and my embarrassment faded as my confidence grew. He also helped me find myself again through ways I never thought of. He would say "there is always a way" when I would get frustrated at a task and be pissed, saying "it can't be done". Somehow he would show me a way.

I remember early on my goal was to make supper but because of my broken arm and very little feeling in my fingers, not to mention very little fine motor skills it was not safe to cut potatoes, onions or carrots without injury so Gary said there is a way! We took my cutting board and drilled a hole in it then put a meat thermometer through the bottom. I then pushed the potato though the metal spear. That held it in place for me and allowed me to cut the vegetables safely and make dinner. To most people it may seem like no big deal but for me it was huge and a big step towards independence. Every week I would learn something new or improve on something old.

Looking back Gary brought me a long way in a short time. Thank you, Gary.

After about two years Gary was offered a job in another city that would be best for him and his family so he moved. I have to tell you my heart blew a fuse when he gave me the news.

Please let this be a bad dream! You have brought me so far and I still have a long way to go ... "how am I going to do this?" I thought to myself.

Along comes Claudia Maurice into my life, my new Occupational therapist and at the same time I received a new case manager, Pat Saunoris. All I could think of was how hard I had worked to get where I was and now I have to start all over again because these new people won't know what is going on in my life. Boy was I wrong!

These two women didn't waste any time steering me onto the path of the straight and narrow, and keeping me on track. All of a sudden it seemed everything was happening so fast. I was enrolled back in high school, and enrolled into driver training which my first case manager did not think I was capable of.

"Thank you, Pat!" I could not believe all of the good things that were coming my way.

The first thing Claudia did with me was to help get me organized. I was so caught up in the never ending trivial tasks that constantly come at you like e-mails, TV and visitors, that I didn't realize how much of a negative impact disorganization had on my recovery. To me it just became a way of life and I accepted it.

Claudia showed me that with very little effort every day I could be organized and very productive with just a little planning. Every day we made a plan as to what I would get done that day. I probably had 20 or 30 things on the list but again Claudia shared with me that I was only setting myself up for disappointment with so many things to do on my list so we started from scratch. In the beginning we agreed there would only be 2 to 3 things on my list to do for the day. It doesn't sound very hard and it isn't, but do you know what happened with those 2 to 3 things? They got done. Doing 2 to 3 things a day gave me a feeling of accomplishment. I finally felt that I was doing something great and working towards a great future. I didn't realize in the past that my huge to-do list with 20 to 30 things on it was just too overwhelming and it really seemed like nothing was getting done, but when I was able to break it down in small chunks I accomplished a lot in a very little time and as my confidence grew I was able to take on bigger tasks feeling good about myself starting a project.

Other things we worked on were returning to the work force in some meaningful way. I am now taking the necessary university courses to become a rehabilitation therapist and I believe I will do very well in that line of work because of my experience over the last ten years. There are very few rehabilitation therapists that can look a person in the eye and say, "I know what you're going through."

"I can't do everything, but I can do something. If we all did something. We could conquer anything."—Robert L Shimmel, Humanitarian

Beware of Rehab Overload

This is a short story of what happened to me, and a warning for you that I hope will save you a lot of time, stress and upset.

When I finally had my mind set that I was going to work on this rehab full-time and be the best that I could be, I was so focused that nothing would stand in my way. I felt like I could take on the world.

Right there was the beginning of a series of problems for me, starting with unrealistically high expectations for a short period of time and then eventually burnout.

In the beginning everything seemed fine. It was all laid out for me. If I do this, this and this, I will reach my goal and solve all of the problems that have been bothering me.

I was self-motivated and determined to give one hundred and ten per cent and believed that anything was possible if I worked hard enough. I still believe that axiom is true but once in a while you have to step back and look at things from a different angle.

Being positive is great, but being realistic will

avoid burnout and failure. So stay positive but also have realistic goals that you can talk about with your rehab workers, family and friends.

When I finally decided to take one hundred per cent responsibility for my life and take control of my rehabilitation it was exciting like starting a new job. I was 'full of piss and vinegar' as they say. Perhaps in some ways I was too anxious with only one focus in mind ... getting better.

After a month or so I started to realize that my expectations were in fact unrealistic. My energy and excitement diminished as did my self-confidence. Along with disappointment came confusion. "Why am I not getting better? I work hard every day. Something is wrong, is it me?" I started to become frustrated and bored with my rehabilitation.

Chronic fatigue became one of my biggest problems. My sleeping patterns had me feeling like a zombie so I was unable to focus on the task at hand. Depression and anxiety also played a part. I kept thinking to myself, "What's the use? I'm trying every day but nothing is happening." A negative attitude became the flavour of the day.

In fact I was trying so hard I pushed my family to the back burner. I found out later that was a big mistake. I wanted to be better so bad that that's all I could focus on during that time. The doctors call that 'perseveration'. Everything in my life was pushed aside so I could get better ,but what I didn't see was that I was indeed pushing my life aside when I should've kept my family right beside me through thick and thin.

I spoke to my doctor about this and he suggested I take a break for a few weeks from my rehabilitation. I did exactly that and boy what a difference. It was almost like stepping out of my own body and having a look around and I have to say I didn't like what I saw.

After that small break I was able to see what was important to me and that I had to keep everything in perspective. My family is number one. My rehabilitation would become number two. I decided to work on my rehabilitation during the day. In a sense, getting better was now my full time job. But like a job, leave your work at work. Don't bring it home for your family especially if you have had a bad day.

Remember that the rehabilitation is about you and your goals. It is important to set goals that fit your needs and not those of someone else. Trying to do and be what others want you to do and be can cause you frustration and burnout.

So spend some time with your family. Most nights I was too tired to even watch television but I learned to lie on the couch with my son because even if I was sleeping I was there with him and I believe that is a great thing.

Getting a hobby or spending time with friends and family is also a great way to relax. Have some fun every day and make sure that your rehabilitation doesn't have an overpowering influence on your self-esteem and self-confidence. Enjoy the journey, have some fun and try not to take yourself too serious.

"It is not the straining for great things that is most effective; it is the doing of the little things, the common duties, a little better and better." —Elizabeth Stuart Phelps, Writer

Vampires and Bandits

Psychic Vampires and Time Bandits

When recovering from a brain injury it is easy to be held captive by the 'psychic vampires' and 'time bandits'. If someone steals your watch or television the police will help with the arrest but with the psychic vampires and time bandits the only crime-fighting tool you have is your mind and you are the only one who can use it. It is purely a state of mind.

A 'psychic vampire' is that person who sucks the energy right out of you. You know, that person who knocks on your door and you answer and see them and think "Oh no, what do they want now?" You feel deflated. Or you answer the phone and they start talking about how bad everything is and you can't even get a word in. When the conversation is over you feel sick to your stomach.

You must avoid these people at all costs and if you cannot totally avoid them just spend considerably less time with them. Just doing that alone will lower your stress level. You should keep your mind closed against all people who depress or discourage you in any way and seek the company of friends and family who encouraged you and who support your goals and dreams. Remember, the easiest thing for others to do is decide what they would do if they were in your shoes. You have to think and act for yourself.

The 'time bandit' is the person who comes around and thinks you have all the time in the world so why shouldn't they help you waste it.?

A lot of times the psychic vampires and time bandits are the same people who want to bore you with "Oh, poor me" stories. And if you get caught up in their trap it only becomes a contest to see which one of you is worse off. Don't fall into this trap. If you cannot speak for yourself let your caregiver or family members know that you do not want this person around. They may have some strategies they can put in place to avoid these unwanted visits or phone calls.

"Time is a non-renewable resource"
—Doug Shaw, Graphic Designer

Control Yourself

The only thing you can control is yourself

I have heard many stories from survivors about how others (parents, kids, spouses and co-workers) will try to control them, their feelings, thoughts, emotions, actions and behaviour. News flash: that doesn't work! It is like pushing a car up-hill with a rope. It won't accomplish anything.

Rather than trying to control a person (which can only create tension), try to make agreements with that person. I found this very helpful. It was my speech language therapist, Christine, who introduced me to this concept.

I don't know if she planned this out or not but she would say things to me like, "Before I come back here on Tuesday can we agree that you will try to read these words I left for you?" I would agree. We did this on a mutually agreed-to basis. She didn't have control over me. What gets controlled or managed is our agreement which is a very mature and respectful way of doing things. From then on we enjoyed a more open and trusting line of communication. It was easier to discuss more uncomfortable subjects and things

I had been avoiding or hiding from. Now that I was accountable for things I no longer felt like a puppet on a string. I had feelings of self-respect and self-responsibility. It was a real confidence booster. When you are treated with respect you want to give some back. It's like the old saying, "Givers get".

One person I met with an ABI told me that his father said to him that he is a disappointment, a failure and a burden on the family. He told me that he couldn't wait to move out and get away from him. You see, his father treated him like a second-class citizen with no respect, trying to control his son and because "givers get", his father was given the same in return - no respect. The son has since moved to another town. I sometimes wonder if they will ever work it out or if the father will die a lonely man without his son at his side. This might be quite different if they had made some agreements with each other.

Looking back, everyone on my team made agreements with me. My doctor had said, "Let's agree that you will not use any tool that operates with gas or electricity" (because of all the incidents I had with tools. I call them 'incidents' not 'accidents' because they could have been prevented if I would have slowed down and assessed the situation). Anyway, I agreed.

My psychologist said, "Let's make a deal. When you feel angry or anxious, go to that quiet place in your head and breathe slowly and relax." I agreed, and after working hard on those things for a few years it would now take a lot to get me angry.

My surgeon told me that if I agreed to follow the physiotherapy plan and I didn't do anything strenuous for a long time that I might be able to keep my arm. "Gee thanks, Doc!" Well, four surgeries later over a spread of two and a half years and wearing a cast on my arm for over two years I was able to keep my arm. It's not very strong but it's there. I kept my agreements and they kept theirs.

These agreements can be made by brothers and sisters, wives and husbands and they really work. If you can put it on paper and sign it, it will make you more accountable because talk is cheap

Agreements can be small or big but it is important to communicate what all parties agree on. Like most people I know we all skipped the mind-reading course in school. So let others know what you are thinking. All people must be present to make the agreement so that everyone knows their responsibilities and everything is on the level. No bullying, bossing or "It's my way or the highway" attitude. All parties must agree - that's why it's called an agreement. It must also be two-sided and not one-sided. You must work with your team; it takes good communication, especially at home where you spend most of your time.

When the home team is working smoothly, home becomes a security blanket in a stressful world. And when it is not working smoothly it can become a source of stress and a place you do not want to be.

You must talk with everyone openly, honestly and respectfully. And they should talk to you in the same way. If you don't talk about your problems they will never get solved. With a lack of communication, molehills will turn into mountains and the longer the silence continues the worse things get. This is why it is important to have a weekly household meeting just so everyone knows where they stand ... who does what chores, who pays what bills and so on.

These types of meetings can easily prevent the accumulation of problems that will bottle up and eventually blow up. With this in mind start today and make your first agreement. You'll soon see the improvement it makes in your life.

"The past cannot be regained, although we can learn from it; the future is not yet ours even though we must plan for it. Time is now. We have only today." —Charles Hummell, Writer

Changes

You may experience changes in behaviour and personality but remember ... the only thing you can really control is your own behaviour. Stop trying to control the lives of your friends, neighbours, partners and families - it will drain you of precious energy and leave you an unhappy person. You can't make anybody do anything. So many of us believe that others can be 'made' to behave the way we want, from closing the fridge door, learning how to control their anger, learning how to speak and communicate, to putting the toilet seat down. Some people use tactics such as guilt, force or bribery to change others' behaviours. These ideas may produce short-term results in behaviour and actions that will last only as long as the pressure is on. For example: following your children around the house and making sure they shut off every light. When you stop correcting them, they stop.

You can't get people to change just because you want them to, or because you think life will be better if they follow your rules. They will only change if they are motivated to do so. We all do things in life for reasons or because of feelings. All behaviour is motivated by payoff in one kind or another. Perhaps you quit smoking because you're expecting your first grandchild and you would like to see him/her grow up. That's a big motivator if I've ever seen one. It probably works better than constantly being nagged at about the cost of cigarettes or your stinky clothes.

The same holds true for rehabilitation. You must look at the positive results that will occur when you work hard on your recovery.

For example, I had lunch this week with a friend I have met that also has an acquired brain injury. He had decided to take the summer off from his speech therapy. When I asked him when he was going to resume it, he said that he had considered not going back because he hasn't seen much improvement. I shared with him the idea that you cannot sit at home and hope to get better at your speech, you must participate every day and that you will not see an improvement unless you do. Hope alone will not provide results. Period. You must have a plan and stick to it. I can understand that you want to take a break from some of the therapies once in a while. It's a healthy idea to step back and look at the progress you've made and the direction that you're going. There were many days I felt that I did not want to do anything but it is also important to get back on track and continue your recovery until you are satisfied, and give up for nothing less.

Dr. Davidson often said to me, "A professional hockey player practices every day for hours and hours. He knows how to skate backwards and how to shoot a puck. Yet they still go out day after day and practice. That's what you must do if you want to be at the top of your game. Whether it is your speech, controlling your anger or learning to drive again, you must have the desire to participate every day."

I know this because I stuck with speech therapy for over five years. Was it all fun and giggles? Not really, especially in the beginning. It was very frustratingly long and boring and made me very tired. I would look at something as simple as an oven and know what it is, point at it, have the word on the tip of my tongue but it would not come out. Pointing at it like a small child. "That, that, that." Yet still, a simple word like 'oven' would not come out. That's frustration and that's what makes a lot of people give up on themselves. "I can't get it, so why even try?" were the thoughts that went through my head. Many, many times.

So often did I want to give up. And this was only because of the emotional pain I was causing myself through my perceived failure. By not being able to read or say the words I was looking at and not being able to remember the ones that I could read and say, it was a very emotional roller coaster. To me it was a long journey and had no end in sight. I just could not imagine being able to read and speak at a level where I would feel comfortable again.

I was very lucky to have someone who believed in me when I didn't believe in myself. I have since seen that person work wonders with others. A friend of mine was in a bad snowmobile accident that left him in a coma for months and also with an acquired brain injury. I went to see his family in the hospital and explained some of

246

the things they might experience when he wakes and all of the wonderful things that would follow. When he came out of the coma he had no speech ability. I recommended my speech therapist, Christine Macpherson, to his family. In the beginning he did not have her but was later able to retain her services.

It has now been about two years since the accident and his speech has improved tremendously but it also is a long slow process. He also practices every day which does not cost anything other than his time and gives him great rewards as he continues to progress every day. But for him, he cannot see the progress.

I explained to him that his progress was like a puppy dog. When someone gets a new puppy they spend many hours a day with it, training and feeding it. For some reason they do not see the progress and growth of the puppy that they are with every day, but then a friend comes over who hasn't seen the puppy in a month and says "Wow, look how much he has grown. It seems like just yesterday that I could hold the puppy in the palm of my hand."

The same thing applies to your recovery. You may not see the small changes every day but if you work daily towards very small improvements it will lead you to massive improvement over time. I made a commitment to myself to change daily in the smallest amount possible – one percent . I would try everyday to improve just one percent a day. It may have been learning a new word or becoming a better father but by improving one percent a day I could do a complete 360 in one year and that was a huge turn around. I continue to try and change one percent a day to this day. Change by the yard is hard, by the inch it is a cinch!

"There are no secrets to success. It is the result of preparation, hard work and learning from failures." —Colin Powell, American Secretary of State

Is Now a Good Time?

Is now a good time to have an anxiety attack?

Depending on its severity, anxiety causes feelings ranging from mild nervousness to doom and gloom or panic.

What's going on?

Anxiety is our biological alarm. When we perceive danger we respond by becoming anxious. A certain amount of anxiety is normal and even productive. For example, if a parent has children playing in the swimming pool and the children have become suddenly quiet the parent may rush to investigate thus possibly preventing an accident as a result of the parent's anxiety. We respond to anxiety emotionally with a complex range of feelings including fear, dread and anger which causes physical responses: tense muscles, racing hearts, shallow breathing and sweaty palms and feet.

Intellectually, anxiety often interferes with clear thinking. Behaviourally, we exhibit the "fight or flight" response, preparing ourselves for self-defence or escape. In the early days this was useful to the individual because when you were in danger it would give you a boost of energy to get away from whatever was putting you in danger, like running away from a bear. Unfortunately, the anxiety alarm sometimes goes awry and we confuse safe situations as dangerous or mildly threatening situations as life-threatening. Many scientists now believe our anxiety alarm system is influenced by a complex interaction of genetics, illnesses, drugs and our history of traumatic events such as a car accident, stroke or being at war.

Panic attacks or anxiety attacks happen anywhere. There is no right time to have one. But they can be prevented.

I remember being in a car and getting short of breath, grabbing the dash and saying, "Slow down!" or "Oh no, we're going to crash!", thinking only of the worst ...or of being in a grocery store and suddenly feeling dizzy and short of breath as if an elephant was standing on my chest. On that occasion I told my wife we had to go. I left the cart in the aisle and ran to the truck where I began to cry. "What the hell is going on in my head?" I thought to myself. The attacks increased in intensity and frequency to the point that I did not want to go into public. I became like a hermit. I would stay home and the only time I would visit people was when they would come to my house. Even the therapists had to attend to me at my house instead of me going to their office. It was almost as if my home was a security blanket.

I would jump out of my skin if the door slammed or a dog barked. I'm sad to admit that for that reason we got rid of our family dog. When hurricane Katrina hit I felt as if I were right there in the TV. I started crying and feeling doom and gloom. "The sky is falling!"

I know now these are common things that happen after a brain injury and there is help and I reached out for that help. "I want to be better", I thought. All of this negative thinking was making me sick. Dr. Davidson reached down and helped me out of this huge emotional hole that I had dug for myself. By showing me how to relax and look at things differently I was able to change my way of thinking.

Relaxation was the key to unlocking the door

that was holding me back. To him I owe a debt that can never be repaid - other than to share with others some strategies on how to overcome anxiety and depression.

I was already on enough pills to choke a horse and I didn't want to take another one for anxiety so I said I would try anything to make this stop. The relaxation techniques worked great. It didn't happen overnight but after a few months I felt great and was able to control the attacks with simple thought, and get back out into the community. Ninety-nine per cent of the bad things I had thought about never happened and the one per cent that did were not nearly as bad as I had pictured.

Anxiety is by definition very uncomfortable, so people who are anxious will at all costs avoid any situation that will make them more uncomfortable. I discovered that this avoidance can have a very serious negative impact on one's life.

One day I was getting coffee and a fellow in the coffee shop shouted to me, "Hey" how have you been? I haven't seen you for a few years. I heard you went a little Coo-Coo for a while from that accident!" I could feel my face turning red. I was angry and embarrassed at the same time. It took all I had not to walk over and throw my coffee in his face. "Relax, Forrest!" I told myself. I just nodded and smiled. Because of my fear of confrontation I was overly nice to people who were not nice to me.

Looking back I can see where that guy was coming from that day. In his eyes I was acting odd, running out of stores crying, avoiding people like the plague, and being alone in my house not wanting to socialize with people. I could certainly see how that would seem odd to someone. So I have since forgiven him for his lack of understanding about what goes on after a brain injury and I later sat down with him for coffee and explained some things I had gone through.

That day I helped him understand and I helped myself understand that there needs to be more information available to the public on brain injury. I know Brian is a decent guy who means well; he was trying to use his sense of humour to break the ice that day, and other than that he didn't know what to say. I told him when we met, "I'm glad I didn't rip your head off and flush it down the toilet" like I wanted to that day.

I still have a sense of humour too.

I hope others can take something from this story and realize people are not mind readers. Try to look at things through the other person's viewpoint like Brian's i.e. what would make him say those things? You must educate them on brain injury so that we can all live a good life. Avoidance is not the answer, it is the problem. It only makes things worse. Consider the sad fact that all over the world people are sleeping on the streets and living in cardboard boxes. They have a million more reasons to believe they've run out of options that you do. So stand your ground and state your case. After the first time you explain your situation to someone it gets easier to do and your anxiety will fade.

If you struggle with anxiety most schools and workplaces will accommodate your needs when you explain your situation. Schools will allow you to take tests and examinations in a quiet room without distraction. Many workplaces may find a different position for you or a quiet place to work but only if it is explained to them that you have a brain injury. They are not mind readers so let people know what is going on as soon as you can so that there is no misunderstanding or miscommunication. In no way should you use your brain injury as a crutch or take advantage of people's kindness, just make them aware of what is going on and things can run a lot smoother and you will have less anxiety.

You may require a note from your doctor which also should not be a problem. Your doctor should be happy should you decide to return to work or school. My doctor was. His only advice was don't beat yourself up and know that you are going to make mistakes and learn from them and I sure did.

"There is nothing so easy to learn as experience and nothing so hard to apply." —Josh Billings, Author

Random Thoughts

Rental vs. Ownership

After my accident I felt like a renter in my own body. What I mean by that is it was a place to live but I didn't really care about it like an owner would. A person who rents a home or apartment may not care if the lawn gets cut this week or if the dog runs through with dirty paws or maybe even if wine is spilled on the carpet. Look at people's attitude towards a rental car vs. the car they own: "It's not mine so why should I care?" attitude. When you have ownership of a home you take pride in it, you cut the lawn, wash the windows and vacuum so when you have company you can be proud of what you own. So as a renter in my own body I didn't take care of myself the way I should have by not eating right or taking care of my appearance and physical health. I just kept thinking that I would wake up in my old body with the old me in the mirror. Well I can say stop waiting for that day. You have to work for it and work hard for your recovery. It's not just going to appear. If you want to chop down a tree it doesn't matter how big it is as long as you take a few chops every day. Eventually it will fall down. The same principle holds true for your rehabilitation. Just work at it every day and eventually you will be where you want to be. You will own your future.

"To swear off making mistakes is very easy. All you have to do is swear off having ideas."
—Leo Burnett, Advertising Pioneer

Buy Now Pay Later

This expression has become a way of life for many. You can enjoy the new car now without paying or working for it for many months and we believe that you can have the reward now and deal with the work later. With brain injury the opposite is true. You must first deal with the unpleasant and frustrating parts of recovery before you can celebrate the victory phase of life.

"You can't learn to swim without getting in the pool".

Delayed rewards means you must work on your problems now no matter how frustrating they are in order to enjoy a good life in the future. Being serious about your recovery must become a habit. A habit is a cable in which each day we weave a thread until eventually it cannot be broken. This holds true for bad habits also, so be careful. I fell into this trap myself. I would lie around on the couch until noon then maybe make something to eat, wait for the therapist to show up and take a rest, and this went on for a long time and became a bad habit. I simply just became lazy and I allowed it to happen.

Fortunately I was able to snap out of it but it wasn't easy. I started exercising a little every day and that helped me regain my energy. There are no quick fixes for anything. Everything takes time, whether it's working on your anger or anxiety or getting out of a rut of laziness. They all take time but if you put your mind to it you can do anything.

Remember if you have the power to begin a habit, you have the power to break it also.

"Only those who will risk going too far can possibly find out how far one can go."
—T.S. Eliot; Poet, Critic, and Editor

Sex, Drugs and Rock and Roll

This story sounds like something you would hear from a rock star but it's a funny personal little story that happened to me.

Sex was different after acquiring a brain injury. For the longest time I had very little desire probably because of the depression and constant pain I was in. It was a very weird time in my life. I was taking so many drugs: Zoloft and Welbutrin for depression, Tylenol three and Percosets to control pain from the surgeries on my face and arm, Arecep to improve my memory, sleeping pills and many others that I don't remember. All the drugs' side effects must have counteracted each other or something. It got to the point I thought my penis was bi-polar. "I want to have sex." "No I don't." When I was in the mood for sex I had to make an appointment so that the Viagra would kick in. It was so embarrassing going to the drugstore to ask for Viagra in my early 30's that I got my brother to drive me to the next town where I would fill my prescription.

This was also a very frustrating time in my life and I compounded my problems out of my frustration. One time I quit taking all my pills because I thought it was ridiculous having to use Viagra because of the side effects of other drugs. "Note to self. Not a good idea!" You see when I quit taking all of my pills for pain and depression I immediately became a miserable person, angry and upset at the world. Who wants to have sex with a person like that? Damned if you do and damned if you don't .

Eventually over the years I have been able to wean myself off all the drugs. But before trying this please consult your doctor. I was able to do this through an exchange program. Yes, an exchange program.

Over a period of time I traded my medication for a pair of running shoes and an ipod. I used to say that I was too stressed to exercise, but little did I know that exercise was one of the best stress reducers ever.

So many drugs.

The other thing that lifted my moods was music (rock and roll). It's amazing just how quickly your mood can change when you listen to some upbeat fast-paced music or whatever makes you smile. The exercise combined with music gave me a whole new outlook on things, and I soon began to see the positive changes I had made.

You can also make these positive changes. Decide today to get up off the couch and go for a walk and just see how good you feel.

I would like to repeat again.

Never stop taking your medication without first consulting your doctor.

"When I examine myself and my methods of
thought, I come to the conclusion that the gift
of fantasy has meant more to me than my
talent for absorbing positive knowledge."
—Albert Einstein, Physicist

Coat of many colors

"Coat of many colors" is a song by Dolly Parton that I first heard as a child. I was only about eight years old but that song stuck in my head all of my life. Perhaps because I could relate to it so well growing up wearing second hand and hand-me-down clothes and remembering other kids laughing at me when I would go to school wearing pants that went well above my shoes.

I think everyone wears a coat of many colours and that one is poor only if one chooses to be. That being said, the same still applies today in our journey with brain injury. We all wear a coat of many colours. The one we are born with is full of energy and excitement, love and wonder, imagination and dreams but sadly after a brain injury so many of us seem to sew on new dark patches of fear and anxiety, stress, doubt and disbelief in oneself. Eventually your coat is covered with these new grey and black patches and we become comfortable in our new coats of fear and doubt and we start seeing things in grey and black believing that there is no hope, so why even try.

When you get so comfortable your behaviour begins to match these self-created ideas of negativity and you will find yourself drawn to others in the same sinking boat and helping them sew on their dark patches. Negativity fertilizes the weeds of depression. So the more patches you sew on the heavier that coat becomes and before you know it the coat becomes so heavy it drags you down.

One is only a victim if one chooses to be. Today would be a good day to take that coat off and start new by shaking off those dirty patches and begin to see those bright colours again. Just look around you. There are so many people who would be willing to help. All you have to do is ask and you'll be amazed how good it feels to have a sense of self respect, well-being and happiness. It is that simple. I didn't say easy, I said simple. Nothing worth doing is ever easy but it can be simple.

Today I am not only a survivor, I am a 'thriver'.

Acres of Diamonds

Russell Conwell gave his speech "Acres of diamonds" more than five thousand times. This story illustrates how Ali Hafed sought riches and fame. He left his home and family to find a diamond mine and he sold his little farm and travelled to Palestine, Europe and at last all of his money was spent. He was in rags, hungry and penniless. He had spent everything in search of precious diamonds. Finally, standing on the shores of the bay in Barcelona, Spain, a great tide came in and he jumped in and drowned.

One day, the man who purchased Ali Hafeds farm discovered something glimmering in the stream. It was a huge diamond. It was on this very farm that they discovered the diamond mine of Golconda. The largest diamonds on earth including the Kohinoor and the Orloff in the crown jewels of England came from that mine.

Had he stayed put and searched in his own backyard (his own mind) he would have found that the riches were already in his possession. Ali Hafed would have had acres of diamonds. He settled for acres of misery instead. He searched the world to find nothing. The riches were right under his eyes in his own backyard.

I hope you can learn a lesson from this story, and know that everything you're looking for and everything you want is all in your head, you just have to find it in yourself.

Don't start looking elsewhere for your happiness. You know where it is.

"You are a Diamond" You are unique
There is no other quite like you
You are precious
You have a sense of worth
You are priceless, You are valuable
You are loveable and capable
Like a diamond you reflect light bringing
warmth and colour to all who see you.

Try a few of these ideas and see how you feel.

- Find someone who needs a hug
- Hand-write some thank-you letters
- Give time to a needy person
- Volunteer in your community
- Call up an old friend
- Open some doors and smile
- Go for a walk with your family.

"Generosity is giving more than you can, and
pride is taking less than you need."
—Kahlil Gibran, Poet and Novelist

Drummond Peet
Prince of the Forest

I first met Drummond Peet about four years ago and he has become one of my closest friends and a great life mentor. I moved to where I live now about six years ago and I would often see Drum on his daily walk up my road with his trusty dog Duffy. I knew Drum was a local retired lawyer from town and very well respected in the community so I did not bother walking out to the road to introduce myself. I often wanted to but I thought why would a busy lawyer like him want to stop and talk to me? Little did I know he thought the same about me.

He told me later that he had heard a lot about me through the business community and someone told him I was a nice guy! But he did not want to bother me as he heard I was a very busy person and why would a young business man want to hang around a retired guy like him?

At this time Drum was unaware that I was recovering from a brain injury and had sold my businesses.

One day a neighbour in an adjoining farm introduced us and we have been great friends since then. I just wish we had met years prior to that date. I have learned so many great life lessons from Drum like always trying to see things from the other person's view point and also to give everyone twenty minutes… don't judge a person in the first two minutes of meeting them because there is always two sides of every person just as there is two sides to every story and many other lessons that have helped make me the person I am today.

Our story reminds me of the childhood movie 'Bambi.' There is little Bambi looking across the forest floor at this large buck, the Prince of the forest, and Bambi says "Wow, look at that large deer with the big antlers, if only I could meet him he could teach me how to survive and fend for myself and escape from the hunters, but why would a big deer like that want anything to do with a little fawn like me?" As the large deer looks back from the top of the hill he says "Look at that young fawn, if only I could meet him he could show me how to play and have fun again! We would have so much fun, I would love the chance to feel young again but why would a young fawn want anything to do with an old buck like me?" Does that sound familiar? So if you want to get to know a person approach them and introduce yourself; you could be amazed at what lies ahead.

And just as the movie plays through, the larger wiser deer (Drummond) is the Prince of this Forrest.

Remember, a stranger is a friend you have not met yet.

Good luck on your journey!

"The art of living lies less in eliminating our troubles than growing with them."
—Bernard Baruch, Government Adviser

I went to the doctor about my memory problem
and when I sat in his office he asked me if the
problem was old or new? I said
"What problem, and who are you?"

I Almost Forgot!

Memory

I can't believe I am finished the book and I forgot to write a part about memory, well actually I do believe it.

I will keep this section short just like my memory. It has been almost ten years since my injury and I still continue to have troubles with short term memory so I have learned some strategies to overcome this little problem. First of all admit it, that will make things so much better.

I will ask people to call and remind me of appointment we may have, I have also become best friends with post it notes they are very helpful if you came to my house you would see them on the fridge, bathroom mirror and coffee maker so I see them often.

I also use different colors and move them from one side of the mirror to the other, if they stay in one spot they somehow become invisible. Another thing that helped me greatly in the beginning were flash cards for kids memory, don't feel embarrassed if it helps it is good.

Day timers and white boards are great also, today most people have them on a phone but I still prefer a good old fashion pen and paper over an electronic device. Don't get me wrong, they are great if you remember to use them. A piece of paper in front of you is the best reminder.

My long term memory is great I think, I still remember being in grade seven and wanting to go to the fall fair but I did not have two pennies to rub together, I was at my friend Jeff's house and I was saying how much fun it would be to go to the fair with all the other kids, Jeff's mother went into her change jar and gave me a roll of dimes five bucks wow, I walked around that fair like a millionaire. That is one thing I will never forget. She was not rich by any means but she had a rich heart and she taught me a lesson that I try to pass on to others.

> "if you have anything to give,
> even if it is merely your time,
> you will never be poor".

*If the human mind were simple enough
to understand, we'd be too simple
to understand it.*
—*Pat Bahn*

Baseballs Don't Bounce